Collected Speeches

 Writings of Donald M. Alstadt

Design and production by Chris Crochetière, BW&A Books, Inc.

Donald M. Alstadt served as the president of the board of directors of the Lord Foundation in North Carolina at the Pratt School of Engineering at Duke University from its founding in 1984 until his death in 2007.

❦ CONTENTS ❦

Beginning in the early 1950s, Mr. Alstadt served as a consultant to the Lincoln Project, which was concerned with the air defense of the United States. In 1956 he was a consultant to the Carnegie Foundation in its efforts to reorganize the technical curricula of American universities.

He was a member of the Swedish Royal Academy of Science, the Faraday Society of London, the American Chemical Society, the Royal Society of Chemistry in England, and the Atlantic Council.

In 1966 he was awarded a patent for Chemlok, which took the Lord Corporation, of which he was to become president and chairman, to the forefront of international surface science technology; and three years later was he appointed by President Nixon as metropolitan chairman of the National Alliance of Businessmen.

He was a guest lecturer before both the International Institute of Management Science Center in Berlin and the Swedish Royal Academy of Engineering Science. He was a visiting scientist at the Massachusetts Institute of Technology, and received the Distinguished Service Award of the School of Engineering from Duke University. He served on the Board of Directors of the National Legal Center for the Public Interest, the National Technology Transfer Center, and the Atlantic Council of the United States.

❡ FOREWORD ❡

Paul M. (Mickey) Pohl

It has now been more than two years since my friend and Mentor, Don Alstadt, passed away. I knew Don for more than forty years, having met him shortly after I entered college. He influenced my life, my thinking, and my views of the world greatly. I miss him. I find myself telling others stories about him; I repeat stories he told me; and I catch myself using his metaphors and favorite anecdotes to make a point. I miss the Sunday morning phone calls. I miss this extraordinary man. But the foreword to this book is not to be a eulogy. For those who knew Don, this volume, which Judy lovingly and fittingly has assembled, will be a wonderful walk down memory lane and yet the latest reminder that Don was not only brilliant but possessed of a multidimensional brilliance. No matter how long you knew Don, invariably you would be in a conversation where you found still another dimension to his knowledge and vision. A conversation with Don was always a learning experience, like an intellectual hike through the Grand Canyon—no matter how many times you had seen it, you always found something new to dazzle you.

For those who did not know Don, I hope you will find this a happy introduction to the life and work of a memorable man. Please know, however, as you undoubtedly will see, that this kind of book can never adequately convey to you the person that Don was; it can only give you, like a great restaurant review, a description of an unforgettable experience—but not the joy of the experience.

So let me set the stage with a few ramblings about Don and how I knew him that may, I hope, contribute in some small way to your enjoyment of this book and perhaps help us better understand the works of this extraordinary man.

I met Don shortly after I graduated from Erie East High School in 1966, from which Don had also graduated about a quarter century earlier. The book *Boyd* about the famous fighter pilot and officer who influenced the design of America's fighter aircraft, post-Vietnam (which of course Don gave me to read), begins with a sentence that declares simply that "Erie, Pennsylvania is a tough town." East High School was undoubtedly the tough school in the tough town.

New York's lower East Side had a reputation that fittingly would also describe Erie's lower East Side: a tough melting pot of many immigrants, poor but motivated ethnic families primarily of European ancestry, a few pockets of successful Anglo-Saxon Protestants, and a significant African-American presence. We were blessed with the diversity experience before America realized it was a developmental blessing. The children of factory workers, policemen, firemen, and the unemployed made great football players (a major part of Erie's culture) where tough economic circumstances made stubborn, determined adults. There were few whiners. This environment was not sugar-coated by today's politically correct standards. Dodgeball, now outlawed in some school districts, was considered one of the tamer gym class activities. What may not have met the eye of a visitor to Erie East High in the late 1930s was the presence of a cadre of talented faculty members, combined with the determination of many parents to have their children go to college and be more than they were.

Throughout his life, Don Alstadt loved talking about East High School. It was not just idle reminiscing about the teen years. For Don, who was always zealous in recognizing and describing the importance of public education in a successful society, the experiences of the many successful East High graduates were like the results of a science experiment—combine talented kids with motivated parents and a few dedicated teachers committed to math, science, and reading and great successes could be produced irrespective of the socioeconomic status of the neighborhood or the relative lack of funding from politicians with low expectations.

Don wrote a few wonderful essays about public education, at least one of which was published in the *Erie Times*. Don could, as usual, "connect the dots." He argued that, for a community to be able to create and hold worthy jobs, even in a manufacturing economy, it needed to have an education system that produced a workforce that could read. Its education system had to convey knowledge and values that would produce an informed, educated, and enlightened electorate. Don explained how many roads in a sound society lead back to a good school system.

The irony here was that, in doing his research for these articles, Don found a memo from the Erie School Board dating back to the late 1920s. It was an educational plan of sorts, tied to the budget process, where the goals for each of Erie's four public high schools were laid out. After providing for language and higher math courses in the other schools, the school district plan described only a basic program for East High, referring to the socioeconomic demographics of the neighborhood and then declaring, as the justification for the poor curriculum, that the students were "educationally terminal." Don wore that like a badge of honor.

When Don became the first inductee into East High's Academic Hall of Fame in the late 1970s, then-principal Viola Andrews, in the induction speech, listed Don's patents, scientific awards, and honorary degrees. Don at the time was one of the few Americans in the Swedish Royal Academy of Science. I told Don that it was too bad that he was "educationally terminal" or he might have made something of himself.

On that occasion at East High, as Don gave his remarks, he described how moved he had been that morning when he came into the front hall of the school building outside of the guidance office and saw that his picture had been hung in the newly designated Academic Hall of Fame. Don noted that this was the space where a picture of George Washington had hung for decades. Proving that the student body had lost little of its irreverent spice, when Don paused after that comment, a student shouted "and George's picture will be back up there by tomorrow morning." The principal was aghast, a teacher collared the kid, and Don howled with laughter.

Don's years at the University of Pittsburgh were magic for him. He loved the whole university atmosphere and he loved being in a laboratory. Throughout his life Don saw, as few others do, that America's great universities, especially through math, engineering, and the hard sciences, are the launching pads for the kind of innovations that improve the quality of life, not just in the United States but around the world. For years, when Don came to meetings in Pittsburgh, he chose to stay in Oakland near the university. Just as he did on the East Side of Erie, Don would walk the neighborhood and savor the memories.

After leaving Pitt, Don began work in the lab at what was then Lord Manufacturing in Erie. Don's breakthrough research in polymer chemistry resulted in the development of the Chemlok line of adhesives that became and have been a cornerstone of Lord for years. Even today, some six decades later, the Chemlok products are used around the world.

Don loved his time in the labs at Pitt, Lord, and, from time to time, MIT. In his later years in Cary, N.C., he had his own office in the lab at Lord's Research Center. He much preferred that atmosphere to any swanky executive suite—although as part of the unpretentious corporate culture that Tom Lord and Don created at Lord, there never was and probably never will be a swanky executive suite.

The history of Lord Corporation is told in the pages of another book and need not be re-told here, but Lord Corporation endures and is unique because Tom Lord and Don Alstadt made it that way.

Tom Lord, a legend in his own right, and Don Alstadt had a bond, a relationship, a shared vision, common values, and an ability to communicate in a way that even the best of friends rarely share. Make no mistake: The relationship between Tom and Don was something special. It's the reason that Lord has endured, prospered, created and sustained jobs, and given so much to worthy institutions now benefited by Tom Lord's unique estate plan.

In the post–World War II era, as Don continued his breakthrough research, Tom Lord and Don were seen as corporate mavericks. Lord did things differently. The company developed a passion for innovation and saw the business world with a longer time horizon. Just as he did in the laboratory—where he could see relationships and reactions before the rest of the world could—Don became the architect of much of what has caused Lord to be different and to survive. What occurred at Lord could only have occurred because Tom Lord had the vision and wisdom to give his unconventional, globe-trotting, insatiably curious scientist, Don Alstadt, the freedom to pursue a different paradigm for Lord.

Don read everything. In his sometimes mismatched green plaid outfits, Don made friends and picked up ideas everywhere. He and Tom resisted the temptation to go public, buy yachts, and hit golf balls. Knowing Don's pride in his Scottish ancestry (he loved to talk about his mother's brogue), I would always remind him that the game of golf couldn't be bad since the Scots created it.

Don's zeal and passion for innovation and technology in general and for the success of Lord Corporation specifically knew no bounds. I saw this for more than thirty years—when almost every week included conversations with Don. I confess that there were times when I didn't understand what he was espousing; I didn't immediately embrace the wisdom of what he was saying (even if I understood it), and there were times when, months or years later, I would grin and concede that Don was ahead of us all and that his vision was spot-on.

In 1975–1976, I was law clerk to Justice Samuel Roberts of the Pennsylvania Supreme Court. Justice Roberts was the first Erieite to serve on the Pennsylvania Supreme Court and later served as the chief justice. I was the first Erie native to become one of his law clerks. That year in Erie was a joy. I loved the clerkship and got to know Don Alstadt—the unconventional science genius who was the new president of Lord Corporation—who drove a VW bus, usually with fishing rods inside, who wore god-awful plaid shirts and suspenders, and who would frequently appear on Saturday mornings in the old East Side neighborhood.

Don, as we all know, could really talk. The unusual thing, however, was that he could genuinely converse with, and enjoy conversing with, almost everyone. He would talk about high school football in Erie with the people at Barney's restaurant. He would talk about fly rods with the fishermen at the dock. He could talk about what was going on at MIT or the Cleveland Clinic and what was wrong with Generally Accepted Accounting Standards. He liked Buckminster Fuller and the breadth of Fuller's genius. I saw Don as Erie's Buckminster Fuller.

When I say Don influenced my life directly, it is no exaggeration. I was a law clerk in Erie because I could not decide where to go to practice law or what kind of law firm to go to. My father, who had been an orphan, also attended Erie East High School and was a well-read and wonderful newspaper photographer. He suggested that I talk to Don and get his thoughts. My dad had not gone to college and we knew few lawyers—but he suggested that I talk to Don because, as my father captured it, "he's smart, you can trust him, he knows people, and he has a vision that goes beyond Erie." That said it all.

Don suggested that I look into what was then called Jones, Day, Cockley and Reavis in Cleveland. He even went out of his way to introduce me to Frank Heath, a Jones Day partner who served on the Lord board. I had no ties to Cleveland and that firm had no lawyers who had gone to Pitt Law School, but I followed up on Don's suggestion. Now, thirty-four years later, I am one of its partners, and it is one of the largest law firms in the world. Thank you, Don.

In the ensuing years, I served with Don on the Jura Corporation board, the Lord board, and as a trustee of the Jura Trust. I saw him in many, many settings. What made Don so different? Let me offer a few insights and anecdotes:

• Don had not only insatiable curiosity but an attention span and memory that were extraordinary. He devoured books and remembered what he read, but he also had the uncanny gift of being able to sort out a passing trend or fad from things that would have enduring value. He knew that W. Edwards Deming's recipe for quality, which the Japanese embraced before Americans did, was going to last. He knew the U.S. auto industry had real problems before the rest of us saw that.

• Don wasn't only a life-long learner, he was a teacher—albeit an unconventional one. Part of a visit to Don was going home with three or four books to read. Part of being on a board with Don was getting books to read, hearing lectures, and occasionally being hauled off to great universities and the Cleveland Clinic for meetings, always coupled with excursions into innovation and knowledge creation.

• Don was absolutely honest, truthful, and incapable of being malicious. It is rare to find a man absolutely without guile. These wonderful qualities were coupled with a lack of desire to acquire wealth or social status. Don knew and taught, usually by example, that character counts and, if you do worthy things well, adequate material rewards will follow. He was incapable of planning a hostile takeover of a business competitor. He and Tom Lord could deal with an employee making a multimillion dollar, good-faith error. They would ask, "What should we learn from this?" Then they would move on. They would not, however, tolerate liars or cheaters.

• Don could use short expressions to convey big ideas. For example: Some companies are overmanaged and underled; it is not good to have too much of your country's wealth coming from one source; it is not enough to do something well, you must be sure that what you *are* doing is what you *should* be doing; profits follow quality, not the reverse; balance sheets don't tell you much because they do not tell you the value of the people or the intellectual property being created; getting great blood test results from your doctor doesn't tell you much about your future if you're in a car that's about to go over a cliff; wealth creation should be important to the future of a society not because it may make a few people wealthy, but because of what happens to many people's lives in the process.

• Don built networks of relationships. Don's range of interests, combined with his sense of humor and total lack of pretentiousness, made him an easy guy to stay in touch with. Football coaches, scientists, professors, maintenance personnel, and casual travelers who met Don would remember him and stay in touch. Don's Erie airport conversation with Hillary Clinton when Bill was running for president—where Don famously asked her if she ever baked chocolate-chip cookies—resulted in Hillary sending him her favorite recipe for chocolate-chip cookies and some memorable correspondence.

Finally, the reader may have noticed that, at the start of this piece when I referred to Don as a "Mentor," I capitalized the word. In Greek mythology, Mentor was the wise, trusted, loyal friend whom Odysseus placed in charge of his son, Telemachus, when Odysseus left for the Trojan War. The name Mentor has been somewhat debased in the corporate world, often being used as someone who merely promotes or supervises another or is a mere tutor. But in the works of Homer, Mentor was the embodiment of wisdom, honesty, and loyalty. The one from whom all should learn. Such people are extremely rare and seldom forgotten.

For me and for many others with whom I toast Don regularly, Don was Mentor.

—Pittsburgh, Pa.
February 2009

George Bugliarello

Donald Alstadt left an indelible impression on those who had the adventure of meeting him during his long life and extraordinary life. My purpose here is not to be hagiographic, but to attempt to introduce the provocative Donald Alstadt as he emerges from this anthology of his writing. He was a true original, his mind always roaming over a vast array of topics, from the conduct of business to society, religion, education, science, and technology. A visionary and brilliant researcher, he became the leader of the company that had recruited him and blossomed because of his brilliant inventions. Out of his experiences, his insatiable appetite for knowledge, his voracious reading, and his cultivation of outstanding scientists, engineers, and leaders, he developed deep convictions and principles, which he was often invited to present to corporations, colleges, universities, academies of science and engineering, and other organizations. Many of them he embodied in a set of red booklets that he distributed prolifically *urbi et orbi*. They have been lovingly preserved by his wife, Judith, and assembled in this volume.

Their wide set of topics ranges from Alstadt's constant concerns about the role of leadership and social responsibility in corporations to the influence of regulation on innovation and entrepreneurship, the relation between a legalistic mentality and national survival, the purpose of the Church, the intriguing query into a faith that would serve us best, and the belief that Systems Dynamics holds the key for rational decision making for the future. These views all reflect the workings and insights of a mind anchored by the pillars of deeply held and seasoned convictions stemming from experiences of people, events, and institutions.

Alstadt's ideas deserve a great deal of reflection by the readers, who, even if they may reach different conclusions, will be stimulated to consider intriguing questions and to challenge some ideas that may be widely taken for granted. The reflections on the myths we live by are a good example of Don's independent thinking, like his observation that the word *democracy* does not appear in the Constitution or in the Declaration of Independence, but that the word *republic* is paramount, or his belief that competition does not always serve the people well, or his attacking the myths that the basic purpose of the corporation is to make money for the stockholders, not the stakeholders, or that children's education should always be pleasurable.

Don ventures in depth into a discussion of the law and endorses the view that we are attempting to deal with current problems and opportunities on the basis of ideologies and perceived needs of previous centuries. He believed that the problems of American society cannot be resolved without fundamental changes in law, but he prudently advocated experimentation with the laws before accepting change.

The major recurring concern throughout his writing and in his life are the questions of leadership and innovation. He strongly expresses his belief that the United States of America is a nation based on innovation rather than reaction to problems. Science and technology are the positive elements of change in the human condition but the world's technological capabilities are not being utilized effectively to alleviate the world's economic problems and suffering. Don believed and practiced the fact that technology stems far more from philosophy and aesthetics than from perceived usefulness and that necessity is not the mother of invention but the product of improvement.

He bemoaned that the chief executives of some major American corporations had not done more to foster innovation—a prophetic statement if one considers the current situation of the American automotive industry. He suggested that to encourage innovation not only in general corporations, but also in technology-oriented ones, the chief executives did not need necessarily an extended knowledge of science and technology, but a sense of enterprise and innovation, and that the average business schools in the U.S. were not adequate to retrain and upgrade the leadership of corporations based on the management of technology.

A tenet of Don's views about the corporation is the importance of making a distinction between leadership and the management. He also states boldly that widespread regulation results in the stagnation of an organization and inhibits American innovation. One might disagree with this concept, but the validity of his observations in the context of technological innovation cannot be disparaged. Don Alstadt was never shy of expressing his opinion. He recounts that when invited to serve on a state board of education, he had sent back a letter with his strong views about education, but never heard back from the board.

A direct connection between Don's unshakable convictions and his corporate leadership was his belief in the importance of establishing in a corporation a strategic committee of the board of directors, which he implemented at Lord. He presents very clearly the concept and its benefits to the corporation, such as matching the "impedance" between the corporation and the outside world, reducing the possible overprotection by management of vested interest in the corporation, instilling in the corporation a learning culture and stressing the corporation's purpose, creed, and mission. Don underscores the need to be concerned with the environment in which the innovation process must occur. To understand that environment and strengthen the ability to make strategic decisions, he believed that systems dynamics, as advocated by some of his heroes such as Professor Jay Forrester, was increasingly dependable and applicable to social institutions and other systems with multiple nonlinear feedbacks.

Leaping from the corporation to the purpose of the Church, Don sees no reason why clergymen should not be involved in social reform, provided, however, that their profession and training should not qualify them as experts, as is the case also for other professions.

Another institution of great concern to Don, an institution to which he devoted a great deal of his energy and intellect, is academe, and its relation with the corporate world. He felt that academe has an important role in addressing the many reasons for the inability of the American industrial corporation to be recognized by society for its true purpose of serving not only the stockholders but also the

stakeholders. In the closing chapter of his collected writings, return-
ing to the question of religion, he asks: what faith would serve us best?
His semipoetic answer reveals another facet, another yearning of this
complex and intriguing personality of our time—a facet hidden even
from those who knew Don Alstadt well.

—New York, NY
February 2009

ONE

Problem-Oriented Lives Threaten Corporate Vitality

M OST OF THE TIME people live problem-oriented rather than goal-oriented lives; they're not really trying to change anything. Many of us are reactive to our environment and its demands upon our life outside the corporate enterprise. We feel reasonably satisfied with our day if we have responded to the demands of other individuals and influences with responsibility, courage, dispatch, and approval.

But this reactive philosophy is not limited to extracorporate areas; indeed, it extends well into the daily corporate mode, affecting not only the individual involved but also entire groups if that person is in a supervisory position. By reacting instead of proacting, by responding instead of directing, the tendency is to minimize risk, assume an immobile position, emphasize conservatism, and maintain the status quo. The sum total is hardly geared to corporate vitality and progressiveness.

This alarming trend runs counter to organizations that have become increasingly aware of a business management procedure, basically designed to manage change. Called by various names—strategic planning, long-range planning, corporate planning, and other colorful synonyms—all such planning suggests the establishment of projected

Originally published in *Daily Journal of Commerce*, April 25–26, 1973, and reprinted in *The Personal Administrator*, September–October 1973, and the *Society for Advancement of Management Journal*, October 1973.

goals for the organization as a whole, and for each division and individual thereof. Nothing could appear more rational and challenging than a management system that so evidently gives various groups and individuals the opportunity to participate in the establishment of inspiring objectives. The system further involves the delegation of responsibility, through the authority hierarchy, to each individual of the organization to achieve those results consistent with his function and responsibility. If each individual fulfills his established goals, the total organization will obviously change and flourish.

After the installation of the "planning process," countless managers are surprised, however, and perhaps even confused and disappointed, that the new approach to operating the organization fails to alter the established habits of many individuals or groups of individuals, and that "old attitude of business as usual" dominates the scene. New planning techniques, meeting schedules, incentive systems, etc. may then be injected into the corporate organism to aid in the transformation. All such procedures may be useful and necessary but such techniques rarely produce the desired rapid transformation in most people's established habits.

Perhaps, however, the most underestimated factors deterring the utilization of planning as an effective management system are a group of human attitudes and habits, often unrecognized, and hence untreated. These, by their very nature, delay the utilization of planning and goal-oriented action by the corporation. There are many such attitudes and I will discuss only those that are common.

The short-term satisfaction of the outside demands, made to the doctor by the patient, to the lawyer by the client, to the politician by the citizenry, to the sales manager by the customer, to the worker by the supervisor, to a person by his family, are the most common motivators for individual action in our society.

The recognizable "accountability" base involves our response to problems provided us by our surroundings and our subsequent evaluation by that environment. The "proactive" thrust demanded of the management of change and effective planning, however, is primarily designed to impact on an environment that probably has not yet invited us to do so. We hope the environment will eventually be pleased with our influence and the changes we are promoting, but, initially, it may be unreceptive and even hostile. Action, under such conditions, is now dependent primarily on the extent of an individual's conceptual view of his role as part of a total effort, his motivation by that view, and his confidence in his ability to pursue his goals—over long time periods with perhaps a minimum of continuous environmental recognition or encouragement.

I do not believe that an individual with little ability to conceptualize and thus project his activity as an important and interrelated part of the total planning effort will ever be highly motivated by formal planning techniques. Even when goals are established by appropriate participative discussion between manager and subordinate, an inability to conceptualize on the part of either person will guarantee little action and accomplishment.

Another common human attitude probably related to our basic "problem orientation" is our tendency, when we plan, to make decisions that will minimize risk. As Peter Drucker has so emphatically stated, "Planning is not a process to minimize risk but to maximize opportunity at a tolerable risk." A problem-oriented organization, however, since it spends a high proportion of its life reacting to outside demands and perhaps crises, finds it very simple to practice "delegation to the top"; the boss makes most decisions, and risk taking by subordinates is certainly not encouraged.

That freedom which must be given to all subordinates—the right to make honest mistakes and learn thereby—so essential to the fulfillment of real opportunity is seldom granted. The appropriate-risk theme of planning, which must necessarily involve mistakes, is not pursued.

A different human attitude that interferes with the promotion and management of change is evidenced by a manager's self-projection as a "knower" rather than a "knower-learner." An all-knowing personality may be great as a consultant, an outstanding problem solver (hence the frequency of the "knower" syndrome in the personalities of the chief executives of reactive, problem-oriented, "delegate to the top" organizations), but such a trait will rarely motivate constructive change in a subordinate or effectively managed organized change in a corporation.

The "learner" image must be present in any individual who would be a good listener, engage effectively in participative management by objective techniques, and lead the change in corporate environment necessary to fulfill corporate objectives never before reached. An ability of any manager to learn and subsequently change himself is probably the most effective technique for insuring willing changes in subordinate habit and behavior.

A number of human attitudes and habits common to many individuals, and prevalent in our society, are inconsistent with the desire of organizations to plan and manage change by objective or goal pursuit. Among these are (1) the basic reactive problem orientation, or "response to immediate environmental demand" orientation, of individuals as the primary motivation to action and reward; (2) the dominating tendency inherent in reactive situations for individuals to enact decisions that minimize risk rather than maximize opportunity; and (3) the likely conditioning of management, whose organizations have long been "problem oriented," to delegate upward with the consequent emphasis and reward for "experience" and knowledge at the sacrifice of any "learner" image.

Changing to the above attitude can require complex proceduring and time-consuming effort. There are, however, a number of simple procedures that might be enacted with reasonable effort. An appreciation of the fact that some individuals are dominantly proactive and conceptually oriented and that other individuals are primarily reactive and eagerly responsive to the short-term demands of their environment is certainly important. The proactive individuals can be moved to such functions where this characteristic is highly necessary—planning, most areas of marketing, research, development, etc. The reactive individuals are most happy in tech service, community service, some aspects of manufacturing, etc.

We should also recognize the fact that the absence of a real purpose or mission with an organization will tend to produce a "risk-minimizing" attitude. Most organizations have a deeper emotional reason for existing than the necessary and motivating objective of making money. When this purpose or mission is clearly understood, opportunity maximizing becomes a more common habit.

A number of universities are currently commencing courses in entrepreneurial management. This type of education program, which, of course, tends to encourage "opportunity maximizing at a tolerable risk," can be more effectively facilitated if we recognize that the establishment of the true purpose or mission of organizations is a must before individuals will depart very far from risk-minimizing habits.

Also, we can encourage employees to recognize that perpetual learning is something vital to the health of the individual and to the health of the corporation, and, as Eric Hoffer has so eloquently stated, "it is a far more noble and necessary function in life than the all-too common attribute of the desire to teach"—a tendency which, I believe, at times creates almost as many organizational and personal problems as it solves.

❧[TWO]❧

Technology and Society

"One of the greatest problems confronting the United States today is the unfortunate lack of awareness, the absence of training and education, and the complete lack of feel and appreciation on the part of most of the people who are operating both our administrative and legislative governments for that technology and science that literally dominates the world in which we live."
— DON M. ALSTADT

When I was asked to comment regarding the future of the chemical industry in Erie, I asked if I could please expand the scope of my talk to include technology in general. I then asked if I could expand my coverage to include society in general. I therefore ended up with a presentation entitled "Technology and Society" and I would like to offer a few comments regarding this subject as seen from the point of view of somebody who is by training a scientist, and who by profession has become a manager and executive.

If I were to have chosen my topic a year ago, I might have adopted a somewhat different approach and included somewhat different coverage. A number of things, however, have happened to our society in

Speech given on the occasion of the fiftieth anniversary of the Erie Section of the American Chemical Society, November 3, 1973, at Mercyhurst College, Erie, Penn.

the past twelve months, and I have been influenced by the impact of these significant events. To demonstrate just how strongly I have been influenced by the events of the recent past, I'm going to close my comments with remarks about Watergate. It is entirely appropriate for any speaker, if he can possibly contrive a few remarks about Watergate, to do so. Everybody now wants to chide about, or just talk about, our political Pearl Harbor. Perhaps the comments about Watergate that I give you this afternoon may be somewhat different from what you have heard before They are, however, directly related to the principal theme that I hope I can develop before discussing the Watergate dilemma.

As has been said, I have a long-standing interest in the subject of management. I have also had a specific interest in the management of technical functions and in the management of organizations wherein technology is the primary base, and the prime mover, in the development of a corporation. Because of this interest, I have become, during the last few years, extremely concerned about the ineffectiveness of the American educational system in developing supervisors, managers, and executives for technology-based organizations. I have relatively little confidence in the ability of most of our business and management schools to develop effective entrepreneurially oriented people for technology-based corporations or as leaders for technology-based society. This conviction has led me, on numerous occasions, to attempt—with the help of the heads of selected engineering and scientific departments of universities (I receive more sympathy from such individuals than I do from most business school professors who seem to be unable to understand the issues involved)—to suggest programs that might be used to develop managers, to develop executives, and to develop entrepreneurs who have a feel for the technology that is so rigorously influencing, and will continue to influence, the decisions and the value systems of the world in which we live.

Perhaps I should define the sense in which I use the word *technology*. By *technology*, I refer to any systematic, organized body of applicable interrelated concepts that is rational and valid enough to stand up under the test of experimental demonstration and experimental validation, and represents a common experience regardless of the society or nation in which it is observed. Technology, in the sense used, not only involves chemistry, physics, and engineering; it also involves medicine, biology, psychology, economics, etc.

This concern for curricula and the training processes that relate to the management of technology and technology-based institutions took me last spring, for example, to a number of institutions in Sweden. Sweden is, incidentally, about as technologically oriented a society as we have on the face of the earth. I desired to determine how the Swedes retrain supervision throughout the careers of such supervision. I was particularly concerned how Sweden managed to keep executives "up to snuff" in both managerial and technological awareness so they could make the decisions that are so necessary in a technologically oriented environment. The first thing I learned was that Sweden has very few business schools; they have few so-called graduate schools of management. Institutions analogous to the American Chemical Society, the American Physical Society, the American Society of Mechanical Engineers, and other professional organizations do most of the managerial training for their members through extensive continuous "outpatient" training programs. Most of the heads of Swedish technology-based corporations are, of course, technologists by education.

While talking with the head of the Swedish Academy of Engineering, I was fascinated that Sweden not only concerns itself with the continuous training of corporate personnel but also trains the members of Parliament in technology-based subjects. Such training, the Swedes believe, is necessary if Parliament is to make effective decisions and plans that regulate and influence the future of their technology-based country. Sweden actually takes the members of Parliament, the elected representatives of the people, and exposes them continually to science and technology seminars so that these representatives are not without a feel, not without an appreciation, not without the necessary understanding required to manage a technologically oriented society. Unlike in the United States, a relatively low percentage of the Swedish Parliament are lawyers by training; such, incidentally, is also true in England and Japan.

Then during the course of the past summer, I spent a considerable amount of time with certain members of our federal government relaying such information to them. As the result of such discussion, it is clearly evident to me that very few, if any, of even the members of our related congressional committees have experienced any significant exposure or education in appropriate fields of technology or science. In a technology-based society, and the United States is certainly such, this condition is both inexcusable and potentially fatal. One of the greatest problems confronting the United States today is the unfortunate lack of awareness, the absence of training and education, and the complete lack of feel and appreciation, on the part of most of the people who are operating both our administrative and legislative governments, for that technology and science that literally dominates the world in which we live.

In the Congress of the United States, we have only one, or perhaps two, certified public accountants and very few professional economists; physical scientists and engineers are almost totally absent. For a technologically based society, this condition represents total incongruity. In this world of continuous change, where effective strategic planning by government is vital to the future of the United States, this absence of technological talent in our government represents an intolerable situation.

As Richard Kostelanetz stated in his superb book *Beyond Left and Right*, "The fault of so much that is publicly presented in the press and passes for radical thought in America today is that it is really just a preoccupation with problems and remedies of an industrial malaise and supposed social inequity that concerned the prophets of a half century ago. In coping with the new realities and radical possibilities, I suggest that most of the ideas that we hear expressed by our lawmakers and our press belong less in our mind and more in our museums.

"We have a need to rethink how we will view radical change in this country, because the final third of this 20th century will be so fundamentally different than anything you or I have experienced, or our fathers have experienced, in the last 70 years—so fundamentally different and so radically different from anything that has ever been proposed by the radical left or the radical right. I think we must be less concerned and interested in what is now common experience, common conflict, or common agreement than in the discovery of uncommon possibilities."

There are new forces upon us in our society—the Soviet military and economic threat, the fantastic information explosion, the great advances in computer technology, the recent and not too distant developments in nutrients and medicine, the expanding field of molecular biology in which, I am sure, we'll find breakthroughs and dramatic occurrences that are just as revolutionary as quantum mechanics, wave mechanics, and the uncertainty principle of the last thirty or forty years. A great explosion of transistorized devices will allow us to do things in miniature and in small spaces that we never could do in macrospaces before. Automation will take a good share of the labor from our backs; limited wars and nuclear capability proliferation will occur throughout most of society and most nations; and last, but not least—something that I am afraid that most people don't realize is now occurring—the application of the new decision sciences, such as operations research and computer analysis, to the evaluation of social institutions and enactment of social decisions. All these new forces are going to create a world unlike anything that we have seen in the past. The environments before us will be shaped by the impact of these future technologies, by material abundance, by greater leisure, by new knowledge about man and his ecology, and by new knowledge about the structure and operation of the human mind. By contrast, the erratical imagination we have seen in the Marxist, in the anarchist, in the liberal, and even the conservative traditions will be of trivial impact. These so-called radical ideas of the past were far too concerned and preoccupied with the dilemmas discovered long ago and with the classic remedies so often tried and practiced that have rarely worked.

The new realities, however, and the new imaginations coming from technology will transgress anything we have heard or anything we have seen. They will literally stagger the human mind. The powers of these new technologies are so fundamental yet so autonomous that a particular crucial machine or device seems to have more or less the same effect on all individuals, on all environments, and on every culture that adopts it. As Kostelanetz states, "This similarity of effect, this history of shared technological awareness is probably the greatest ecumenical force in the world today."

Some people fear technology, failing primarily to recognize that it is a body of practice based upon a body of rational human knowledge constituted by rational human beings. Marshall McLuhan's dictum that there is no possible protection from technology except new technology, that the process of technology will save us from technology, and that to this process there is no limit or no end must be heeded. It is a situation with which we had better learn to live and I suggest we learn to enjoy. The ultimate enemy is not the new machine but a panoply of old ideas that keep us from using all the new machines, mechanisms, and devices as propitiously as we might for the benefit of all mankind. I know such ideas are not shared by some young people and by many individuals publicly expressing their views. I believe, however, there is little technological advance that we have seen in our lifetime that has not saved us from worse difficulties and miseries than the new technology has created.

We hear so much conversation and comment these days about pollution, the horrors of pollution, and its effect on our life, on mankind, and on our cities. I remember a number of years ago standing in front of a statue in Vienna and witnessing the fact that in the sixteenth or seventeenth century, 80 percent of that city had died from the plague in a period of about fourteen months. Now that is pollution. Today, in our western industrial society, we have no such assaults by nature on mankind. To eliminate such difficulties as exemplified by the Vienna plague, it didn't require soothsayers, it didn't require critics of civilization, it didn't require critics of progress—it required an advancing scientific and medical profession. It required the lives of people like Pasteur and Koch. In this country, it required the growth of a very active and competent drug and medical industry. No one, if they rationally think about the matter, would prefer the worldwide biological pollution of yesterday to the urban chemical pollution of today. Such, however, is no excuse for technology not eliminating the latter and I have little doubt such will be done. We should remember, however, that nature's pollutants—namely diseases transmitted by mosquitoes—are still the largest cause of human fatality in the world.

We are beginning to realize that the ideas that were radical two decades ago are archaic today. Perhaps we are beginning to recognize that the wisdom of our time must be more transitory and metamorphic than metaphoric and that no principle is as much a cause of human social distress as the information lag, which I define as a discrepancy between what is now known and ultimately useable and what is actually practiced through much of the world.

Unfortunately the people who are responsible for the ultimate decisions and policies governing the actions of our people, and who also make the publicly observable decisions in our society, are not aware, for the most part, of this lag discrepancy. They are not aware of what is possible and what is feasible in a relatively short period of time. Buckminster Fuller has commented that this widespread information lag is at the root of the world's failure to solve its poverty although it is now possible to provide 100 percent of currently living humanity with the necessary material needs of life.

We must realize that the enemies of progress are those who hold vested interests in obsolete forms and those who hold vested interests in obsolete practices, obsolete technology, and, most importantly, hold vested interests in archaic ideas. To again quote Kostelanetz, "Perhaps the truth is all too obvious—that the greatest vested interest today is not property, but ignorance and the resulting inability to curtail the time between the conceptual presentation of an idea and the enactment of the utility of that idea for the benefit of a large segment of the human race."

We must recognize a few characteristic impacts of the new technology. One of the fruits of a technological society is the realization that the world's wealth is not a fixed quantity and that technology is primarily responsible for a material abundance that allows America to tolerate, if you will, one-fourth of its population as professional students. We must recognize the continuation of the growth of technology means the continuation of growth of material and wealth equity. Science continually does more with less; wealth is created. This is contemporary magic, and the utilization of nature in the organization of knowledge, and the subsequent application thereof, is the primary method by which the magic is accomplished. As Julian Huxley so vividly claims, "The creation of knowledge through the evolution of the human brain is the only inexhaustible resource with which man has to work." James Bryant Conant has made the observation that the most significant progress comes not from the empirical fondling of old problems but from the opportunistic exploration of new concepts, new theories, new ideas, and new information. The future results of our knowledge explosion are going to be most dramatic; we have already seen some evidences of its impact. As the information lag is shortened, we shall have an increase in leisure time for all, and poverty that politics can't cure will fall to the spoils of abundance. Although my Calvinistic ethic winces at the thought, I am sure the annual wage to everybody, whether they work or whether they don't, will be a reality within our lifetime. The development of new educational methods and teaching machines may radically change the entire learning process, and learning may well become the primary aim of life; education will be this country's largest industry and will promote a revolution within man himself; the reforming of society then will parallel the changes that occur within the individual. Science will not only have lifted burdens from man's backs; it will lift burdens from men's minds. This new society, geared to learning, will be able to absorb more of the inevitable continuing change, and be more resilient in accepting change, than a society which is not so devoted to learning.

As technological progress proceeds and man shortens the lag period in which it is utilized, new value systems will occur. It shakes our convictions to realize that our value systems do not organize, restrict, and direct technology; to a large degree, technological advance changes our value system. Our attitude toward sex, our attitude toward birth control, and our attitude toward human behavior have probably been influenced more in the last ten years by "the pill" than any other singular influence in the recent history of man. We can repeat analogous examples over and over again.

A member of the press asked me, a number of weeks ago, who were the real leaders of society. He was a little bit annoyed, a bit chagrined and surprised when I didn't mention the John Kennedys and the Richard Nixons, because I think the people who are really leading this society in the direction it is going are selected people that most of society never hears about. I can remember the day John Von Neumann died; there was a little section in my local paper, way down in a corner, "John Von Neumann, Princeton, New Jersey, Eminent Mathematician, died today." I don't think there is any doubt about the fact that John Von Neumann has, or will have at least, indirectly influenced the lives of more people in this room than any politician we have in office. Eugene Wigner, whom you don't recognize unless you are familiar with the world of physics and physicists, has probably influenced more scientists and technologists, who then in turn have influenced the growth of more areas of technology, than anyone who is still alive.

One individual you may wish to watch; he may be the Pasteur of our current generation of social ills. I refer to Jay Forrester of the Massachusetts Institute of Technology. His writings on social organizations and methods of programming them for mankind's benefit are beginning to dramatically influence the way we look at our social institutions. His classic article on the "Counterintuitive Nature of Social Organizations" has shocked many individuals and "do-gooders"; Jay Forrester contends, as the result of his "systems technology" study of social organizations, that many of the things that we intuitively do to solve our social problems will actually make them worse.

The people who "lead" our world of innovative thought have a number of characteristics—they have a power to initiate and subsequently direct their attention to unexpected possibilities; they have the power to plan, and as Peter Drucker said, "strategic planning is the vehicle by which information lags are shortened and put to work for the benefit of mankind."

Herman Kahn has stated, "Planning must be supra-political because the use of technology, for the benefit of society, by utilizing a planning methodology, is something governments cannot do. Governments are not currently staffed with the kind of people who even understand the concepts of long-range strategic planning. All that such individuals can usually do is respond to the day-by-day crises. Most of the real planning will have to be done by industry, by the universities, by non-profit organizations, and even by individuals themselves." Buckminster Fuller has said that "to ask a politician to lead us is like asking the tail of a dog to lead the dog."

One particular gentleman, working in a university many years ago, said, "The practical man assumes that he is not influenced by the world of abstract ideas, but in reality, the practical man is influenced by nothing else but the world of abstract ideas." Unfortunately, the idea usually occurs twenty-five years before the so-called practical man is influenced by it. The man that made this statement was John Maynard Keynes. Most "practical men" in our society (and particularly our politicians) are tossed back and forth by the economics which Keynes professed during his time.

Most social and political revisionists talk, of course, about changing our system. These people fail to realize that our system is changing continually under the influence and pressure of ideas and technology. Most transformations occur outside the world of politics, which in today's world is really less of an initiating force than an adjusting operation basically providing regulations to cope with the changes that are already occurring.

Unfortunately, government's influence can perhaps only be one of restricting natural progress rather than progressively assisting the application of knowledge to human and social advancement. The less knowledgeable a political regime is, the less aware it is of new knowledge and technology, the more reactionary, the more laggard it becomes and the more irrelevant are its politics. It is, of course, unfortunately effective in extending the period during which the citizens ultimately achieve their inevitable future; perhaps all we can really do is reduce to a minimum this ability of government to increase "information lag."

Technology, not government, has produced a generation that is more skeptical about war, more enthusiastic about the possibilities of machines, more tuned to computers, less desperate about accumulating wealth or conspicuous signs of wealth, more open to ideas, more tolerant of eccentricity, more committed to sweeping social change, less concerned about what it can get out of life, and more concerned about how it can make the system work.

Our technological traditions are shaping a new thought, a "change ethic," as Donald Schon calls it, and its exponents do not descend from any common intellectual base. Peter Drucker, a conservative, speaks of a radically different future. Zbigniew Brzezinski, the violent anticommunist, now says that communism is less of a threat to the United States than ideas that are out of date.

The new technology is nonutopian, nonidealogical—it doesn't offer final definitions but imaginative suggestions. It offers mind-expanding paths rather than mind-limiting walls. It is based on the notion that the more progress we make, the more we will have to make. Such is what I think is going to happen within the next thirty years and we as citizens can either decide that we are going to be annoyed by it, destroyed by it, or enjoy it.

Most of us in management realize that if we are going to plan and manage an organization, if we are going to plan and manage the opportunities, if we are going to plan and manage events, and not be managed by them, we must have a conceptual awareness that transcends the events of today. We must be able to place the things that are going on around us at the moment in a more extended time frame. We must be aware of the knowledge base and technology that is influencing the organization, indeed governing the organization that we are attempting to manage. One of the most vital qualities of leadership today is the ability of a man who is running an operation to have a clear concept of "what the future could be like" in view of the technologies that dominate his organization. This ability is indeed that necessary motivating and charismatic quality that Berlew depicts as so significant, and must be added to the managerial posture pursued by our business schools. In closing, I would like to make the promised comments regarding my interpretation of the Watergate situation.

In a society in which 60 percent of the Congress comes from a profession that is geared primarily to gauge what is applicable today essentially in terms of what was useful yesterday, namely the legal profession, it is no wonder that such people, when placed in jobs, either in the administrative or legislative components of our government, are finding it increasingly impossible to feel comfortable, to feel self-assured, to feel confident, that they can plan or influence the future of this country by the correct selection of conceptual conviction, by the appropriate level of conceptual legislation, by the right degree of conceptual decision.

Most of us fail to realize that a lawyer is really able, by his training, to do only two things—important as they may be. He is able to draft a regulation or a law after somebody with expertise in some knowledge area or technology has designated what particular conception horizon should be expressed. He is also, of course, able to investigate, prosecute, defend, or judge a situation in view of established regulations or existing law. By training, he is not prepared to handle the varied conceptual trends and the conceptual realities in a wide spectrum of human knowledge or experience.

Today in the United States, as technological a society as any in existence, we have a most unfortunate situation. During the past five years of the Nixon administration, but certainly not limited thereto, we have witnessed most decision-making functions carried out by groups of people who represent a profession to whom technology, in its broad concept and character, is a completely unknown and a completely awesome thing.

If you move around Washington with any degree of frequency, you will rapidly become aware of the relative ignorance on the part of most of our elected and appointed representatives regarding this technological world in which we live. Most of them are trained in a manner which suggests that to see around the next corner, they should study the rearview mirror. They are trained in a profession which is oriented toward problems, traditions, and adversaries, not opportunities. They are concerned primarily about the concepts that were appropriate or existent twenty years ago, not what new concepts have been born that now appear to be radically opportunistic.

If our nation is to be opportunistically in tune with the changes that are inevitable, if it is to predicate by effective planning and management the use of new technology rather than being injured by it, we must in some way generate the ability, within our governments, to handle the new information that lies before us.

Watergate exemplifies a situation wherein people were placed in responsible jobs for which they had no conceptual ability and in which they had absolutely no innate feeling of competency. Individuals from industry know what happens when such occurs. One of three things happen: individuals so placed may, of course, realize with honesty they don't have it, they can't "cut the mustard," they quit. Secondly, they may, of course, go off to a corner and hide, hoping that nobody places them in a position where they have to make a decision. Finally, if the individual has a strong ego and other augmenting emotional characteristics, he may begin to change the laws of the game. He begins to play the game of politics; he begins to play the game of power. A new self-assumed "role" replaces his legitimate and expected functional performance. A man with a strong ego, who has no sense of competency in the area of knowledge that he is supposed to lead, certainly has this alternative if he is to opiate that ego; unconsciously or deliberately, he can play the power game. Such is what happened to certain members of the Nixon administration.

Although their actions may be characterized by more legality, many members of Congress are also succumbing to the same "role replacement of legitimate function"; they are delighted with the opportunity to investigate, prosecute (or defend), and judge the executive branch of government. They are now "doing their thing." The challenge of strategic conceptual planning, if they ever recognize the need for same (and the legislative formulation resulting therefrom), never caused them anything but frustration.

Watergate-like events will happen again and again if we don't succeed in placing people in government with knowledge and conceptual ability so necessary for enacting the vision and functions that we expect them to perform in our changing technological world.

The progress of this country must be influenced by people with knowledge; it must be influenced by the people who understand the basic technological concepts that can lead us to the fulfillment of the opportunities that confront this country; I hope that in some way we can, in the future, find a way to place increased numbers of technically oriented people and scientifically trained individuals, also possessing leadership and managerial aptitudes, in both the administrative and legislative areas of our government. If we do not find a vehicle for so involving such individuals in our governmental decision process, the described information lag will become so extreme and debilitating that our society will certainly suffer.

THREE

Participative Programs That Have Improved Sales and Marketing Performance

I N MY ROLE as a corporate president, one of the most difficult problems with which I must wrestle is maintaining the dynamicism and original excitement of an idea as it descends the corporate chain of command. I am not speaking about tactical decisions; hopefully, such executive orders are accurately and swiftly carried out by well-functioning departments or units. Rather, I am concerned with strategic concepts—ideas that require enthusiasm and imagination by those delegated to see them through. In this area in our company, and probably yours, there is unfortunately still considerable room for improvement.

The strategic order can be vital to the lifeblood of a corporation. For strategy—which precedes tactics in almost every case—dictates the various marketing, research, and production roads down which a corporation travels in its daily routine. Yet strategy is most vulnerable to the individual dictates of those assigned to carry them out. Unless there is total communication between all levels of responsibility—unless there is thorough understanding by subordinates in what must be done and when—and unless there is unabashed enthusiasm by every-

Speech given at the 1973 Marketing Conference of the Conference Board, October 18, 1973, at the New York Hilton Hotel.

one connected with the idea, the strategic order must fail to achieve its complete success.

Today, I would like to share with you two strategic concepts which I believe will enhance the marketing performance of the strategic command. Before discussing these concepts, permit me to first discuss the procedure by which full participation is supposedly achieved in the appreciation of strategy and in the establishment of objectives by a unit of corporate organization—be it a company, a marketing division, a sales department, or whatever.

Let's assume that this group is managed by an individual who has a number of subordinates reporting to him—with each subordinate in turn responsible for some component of the total group function. If the group is the Marketing Division, the marketing manager could have as subordinates a sales manager, advertising manager, and perhaps a market or commercial development manager. Other departmental groups would have individuals with different titles, but roughly the same subordinate roles.

In our example, the marketing manager can deal with his subordinates in two participatory ways in the discussion and establishment of goals and objectives. This "boss" (I dislike the word, but it certainly is descriptive) may confer with each of the individuals separately, going over similar grounds repeatedly, or he may confront them as a group and portray the task before them as the establishment of objectives for the Marketing Division as a whole. In my opinion, there is no doubt as to the superiority of the second approach over the first. For the plain fact is that the group-discussion concept is far superior to the individual-basis procedure in *facilitating the effectiveness of the strategic order.*

Why? Because conferring with subordinates one-at-a-time does not establish true divisional objectives, leaves the subordinate out in the cold regarding the intent of his peers, and confuses lines of communication due to alteration of the fact through repetitive conversations. The one-at-a-time approach has basic flaws in it even under the best circumstances. We can assume that the "boss" has excellent desk and office manners, that he thoroughly listens to his subordinates' views, and that he encourages discussion. Then, seeking to maintain the appropriate balance between "what" and "how" demanded by all students of management and proponents of delegation, our "boss" eventually approves the objectives and goals for the subordinate's organization, priding himself that he has appropriately retained the "how" for subordinate decision. He then moves to another subordinate, repeats the same procedure, and subsequently generates a conviction that he has, with each subordinate, enacted sound participatory techniques and established a group of objectives with each associate that reflects the correct balance of "what" and "how."

This scenario is fairly common in American industry. Many executives, because of their basic emotional nature, would rather deal with subordinates on a one-to-one basis. Many simply avoid dealing with the subordinates as a group. The objectives of the Marketing Division, in our example, simply become the sum of the objective of the subordinate departments. In reality, true Marketing Division objectives have not been established and the subordinate is guided almost solely by his own organization's intent. He is certainly not very familiar with the intent of his peers.

Dealing with subordinates on an individual basis during a participative planning process fails to provide all members with the most important and vital participative experience: the appreciation of how each subordinate and his organization has become a part of and enacts to support those objectives of the total group of which the subordinate and his peers are a part, and for which the "boss" is primarily and directly responsible.

The second, vastly superior method—confronting subordinates as a group—portrays tasks as the establishment of objectives for the Marketing Division as a whole. Our "boss" should accept as rational only those objectives to which each and every subordinate and his related organization must significantly contribute if the Marketing Division is to achieve its goal.

An objective to book $10,000,000 in orders for 1974, for example, is a rational objective for the Marketing Division only if each of the subordinate managers and their groups (Sales, Sales Administration, Customer Service, Commercial Development, etc.) can express and establish significant subobjectives for themselves, the enactment of which is vital in the achievement of the booking. If only, per chance, the efforts of the Sales Department can really influence the booking in question, the $10,000,000 booking should be a Sales Department objective and not an objective of the Marketing Division.

The somewhat unrealistic example is merely given to cite a principle: that the participative methodologies that are most effective must (1) establish objectives for an organizational unit, the achievement of which must involve the efforts of each subordinate after the "boss" has accepted those objectives, and (2) provide the subordinate with an appreciation of how his organization must work in harmony and synergism with those of his peers if the objectives, in our example, of the overall Marketing Division, are to be achieved.

The subordinates may, subsequently, working together as peers, either in the absence or presence of the marketing manager, or "boss," decide how they will establish mutually supporting subobjectives that will enable the fulfillment of the Marketing Division's primary ones. They are, in effect, participating with each other, as well as with the "boss," in the enactment of the total participative process. The "boss," after analysis of this peer participation, has only to justify that the subordinates' subobjectives are mutually augmenting and each supportive of the Marketing Division's primary goals. This is true participative procedure—it has the added advantage of promoting peer cooperation and, in addition, peer pressure for accomplishment, peer dissatisfaction for low performance, and peer approval for satisfactory results.

This fully participative interplay between the "boss" and his subordinates, involving discussion and decision-making processes between (1) the "boss" and the subordinates present as a group, and among (2) the subordinate peers working in the presence or absence of the "boss," demands, however, the existence of a compatible level of "conceptual ability" of each subordinate peer and a higher level of such capability for the "boss." We have all heard about the hierarchy of objectives for an organization wherein each subordinate organization has objectives that are "umbrellaed" by those of the higher level organization of which it is a part. We are told that each "hierarchy of objectives" is accompanied by a corresponding "hierarchy of responsibility ladder." We are rarely aware, however, that to make these objective and responsibility hierarchy ladders work, we must find a well-developed "hierarchy of conceptual abilities" present in the organization. If, for example, the marketing manager's conceptual ability is lower than that of one or more of his subordinates, the full participative "management by objectives" process will have "tough sledding" in group discussion. Perhaps this type of deficiency in the "boss" is one reason for the common habit of planning by the boss-subordinate "one-to-one" process initially discussed. Nevertheless, the rewards forthcoming from establishing organizations staffed with people of adequate conceptual breadth who will, in turn, engage the "full group discussion" participative process more than justify any effort or trauma involved in personnel change.

Now I should like to discuss the two strategic concepts which, if appreciated by all of the members of an organization, contribute much to the ease with which compatible decisions are forthcoming in any participative process. I believe these "appreciations" are particularly necessary in the marketing component of a business, which is continuously exposed to a large number of external influences that are at times distracting and even diverting.

The first appreciation, to which far more attention should be paid by both marketing and top management, is an awareness, on the part of the members of the organization, of the basic purpose of the total corporation. Many of my colleagues would answer this statement by stating, "Why, the basic purpose of any corporation is to make a profit." Some may take a somewhat broader economic viewpoint and include the growth of stockholder equity or even the total community economic well-being. While I agree that these economic factors represent motivating, necessary, and (for most of us) very useful objectives, I do not believe they represent the basic driving spirit behind the existences of most corporations. If they did, many American corporations, during most economic periods, would, if true to their basic purpose, liquidate at book value and reinvest in a gambling casino or at least in tax-free municipal bonds.

It is usually not a simple matter to ascertain the basic purpose of a corporation. It may be locked in the mind of its founder-chairman or in the value system of the chief executive officer. The corporate purpose may be more apparent in the decision habits of the top management than in any written or publicly expressed format. Let me cite two examples. An industrial psychologist, who had as a client the number two organization in size of a particular American industry, told me that his client obviously was motivated only by a desire to emulate the number one company of its industry. Nothing precipitated decision and action of the part of his client like an apparent initiating action of the part of the number one competitor. Number two would always immediately follow number one's course. To the psychologist, the purpose of organization number two was to be just like organization number one. I do not care to justify or criticize this purpose. It was simply a fact of life and I'm sure much of the planning and objective setting in organization number two was strongly influenced by the purpose it had probably unconsciously adopted.

Much of the American aerospace industry has had, during the past quarter century, a purpose that might be defined as the development and collection of technological and productive capability that would effectively promote the defense, military, and, at times, civilian interests of the government. Certainly the companies, the government, and society have acted as though this were so.

Not all "purposes" are as easy to define as the two cited. When the purpose of an organization is clearly established and expressed to employees, however, dramatic things may happen. One organization with which I'm very familiar has adopted Donald Schon's "change ethic" and established the following purpose:

"It is the primary purpose of the corporation to maintain a unique identification within all of industry by 1) promoting the full utilization and inter-relationship of advanced knowledge and disciplines and by 2) constantly promoting constructive deviation from established practice or standards, to create and maintain a real leadership identity."

After adoption of this purpose and, within a relatively short time, changes occurred throughout many divisions of the organization, particularly within the Marketing Division. Many individuals found the expressed purpose highly motivating and challenging; others found it emotionally intolerable and incompatible with their value systems and lifestyles. Some of these latter individuals actually left the company and were replaced in their jobs with either existing or new employees who like the new corporate theme.

The common appreciation and acceptance of a corporate purpose attracts and binds people of like value systems, habit, and motivation. It does much to make the participative process an experience of common dimension. It produces objectives among corporate groups that display compatibility and synergism.

Another strategic concept in appreciation requiring top management, and certainly marketing manager, attention is the establishment within the minds of all employees of the organization—the Marketing Division in our case—of a sense of "what the future could be like" and "what it will be like" if the total organization desires to make it so.

In his superb paper "Leadership and Organizational Excitement," David E. Berlew designates leadership types as custodial, managerial, and charismatic. The custodial leadership approach is primarily concerned with things like equal opportunities, decent supervision, compensation, etc. The managerially oriented leadership approach is, of course, the approach we have been exposed to as executives for the past twenty years. It includes job enrichment, job enlargement, management by objectives, and participative techniques. Berlew would certainly not ignore or eliminate the custodial or managerial approaches. He would, however, augment them with a charismatic input, based primarily on the full appreciation by all members of the organization of "what the future could be."

I am knowledgeable of one organization, namely ours, Lord Corporation, that has depicted in words the characteristics and image of the corporation as the management expects to find it ten years hence. The nature of the product line, technology base, type of organization, size, profitability, geographic and market character are all described. The intent of this description of the future is the establishment of a common vision that will provide a mutually understood base for participative procedures and the selection of objectives. The effect of this future image construction is subtle but certainly pronounced.

Human Knowledge, the Legalistic Mentality, and National Survival

The author explores the problem of nontechnologically trained or oriented governmental and legislative figures who must make critical decisions while suffering from an information lag. The impact of this historic weakness in our free enterprise system is analyzed in the light of modern technological concepts.

If the present Congress errs in too much talking, how can it be otherwise in a body to which the people send 150 lawyers whose trade it is to question everything, yield nothing, and talk by the hour? That 150 lawyers should do business together, ought not to be expected.
—THOMAS JEFFERSON, AUTOBIOGRAPHY

During the past several years, I have had a specific interest in the management of technical functions and in the management of organizations wherein technology is the primary base, and the prime mover, in the development of a corporation. Because of this interest, I have become, during the last few years, extremely concerned about the ineffectiveness of the American educational system in developing

Speech given to the Federation of Societies for Coatings Technology, October 29, 1975, Los Angeles, Calif.

supervisors, managers, and executives for technology-based organizations. I have relatively little confidence in the ability of most of our business and management schools to develop effective entrepreneurially oriented people for technology-based corporations or as leaders for a technology-based society. This conviction has led me, on numerous occasions, to attempt—with the help of the heads of selected engineering and scientific departments of universities (I receive more sympathy from such individuals than I do from most business school professors, who seem unable to understand the issues involved)—to suggest programs that might be used to develop managers, to develop executives, and to develop entrepreneurs who have a feel for the technology that is so rigorously influencing, and will continue to influence, the decisions and the value systems of the world in which we live.

This concern for curricula and the training processes that relate to the management of technology-based institutions has taken me, for example, to a number of institutions in Sweden. Sweden is, incidentally, about as technologically oriented a society as we have on the face of the earth. I desired to determine how the Swedes retrain supervision throughout the careers of such supervision. I was particularly concerned how Sweden managed to keep executives "up to snuff" in both managerial and technological awareness so they could make the decisions that are so necessary in a technologically oriented environment. The first thing I learned was that Sweden has very few business schools; they have few so-called graduate schools of management. Institutions analogous to the American Chemical Society, the American Physical Society, the American Society of Mechanical Engineers, and other professional organizations do most of the managerial training for their members through extensive continuous "outpatient" training programs. Most of the heads of Swedish technology-based corporations are, of course, technologists by education.

While talking with the head of the Swedish Academy of Engineering, I was fascinated that Sweden not only concerns itself with the continuous training of corporate personnel, but also trains the members of Parliament in technology-based subjects. Such training, the Swedes believe, is necessary if Parliament is to make effective decisions and plans that regulate and influence the future of their technology-based country. Sweden actually takes the members of Parliament, the elected representatives of the people, and exposes them continually to science and technology seminars so that these representatives are not without a feel, not without an appreciation, not without the necessary understanding required to manage a technologically oriented society. Unlike in the United States, a relatively low percentage of the Swedish Parliament are lawyers by training; such, incidentally, is also true in England, Japan, and Germany. In most industrial countries, the number of lawyers in the central legislative electorate rarely exceeds 5 percent. The Congress of the United States has a lawyer "density" of about 60 percent.

I have recently spent a considerable amount of time with certain members of our federal government relaying such information to them. As the result of such discussion, it is clearly evident to me that very few, if any, of even the members of our related congressional committees, have experienced any significant exposure or education in appropriate fields of technology or science, or are interested in acquiring such exposure. In a technology-based society, and the United States is certainly such, this condition is both inexcusable and potentially fatal.

Perhaps I should now define the sense in which I use the word *technology*. By *technology*, I refer to any systematic, organized body of applicable interrelated concepts that is rational and valid enough to stand up under the test of experimental demonstration and experimental validation, and represents a common experience regardless of the society or nation in which it is observed. Technology, in the sense used, not only involves chemistry, physics, and engineering; it also involves medicine, biology, psychology, economics, etc.

In the Congress of the United States, we have only one, or perhaps two, certified public accountants and very few professional economists; physical scientists and engineers are almost totally absent.

For a technological-based society, this condition represents total incongruity. In this world of continuous change, where effective strategic planning by government is vital to the future of the United States, this absence of technological talent in our government represents an intolerable situation.

There are new forces upon us in our society—the Soviet military and economic threat, the fantastic information explosion, the great advances in computer technology, the recent developments in nutrients and medicine, and the expanding field of molecular biology—in which, I am sure, we'll find breakthroughs and dramatic occurrences that are just as revolutionary as the quantum mechanics, wave mechanics, and the uncertainty principle of the last thirty or forty years. A great explosion of transistorized devices will allow us to do things in miniature and in small spaces that we never before could do in macrospaces. Automation will take a good share of the labor from our backs; limited wars and nuclear capability proliferation will occur throughout most of society and most nations; and last, but not least—something that I believe that most people don't realize is now occurring—the application of the new decision sciences, such as operations research and computer analysis, to the evaluation of social institutions and enactment of social decisions. All these new forces are going to create a world unlike anything that we have seen in the past. The environments before us will be shaped by the impact of these future technologies, by material abundance, by greater leisure, by new knowledge about the structure and operation of the human mind. By contrast, the erratic imagination we have seen in the Marxist, in the anarchist, in the liberal, and even the conservative traditions, will be of trivial impact. These so-called radical ideas of the past were far too concerned and preoccupied with the dilemmas discovered long ago and with the classic remedies so often tried and practiced that have rarely worked.

"We are beginning to realize that the ideas that were radical two decades ago are archaic today," as stated by Richard Kostelanetz in his superb book *Beyond Left and Right*. Perhaps we are beginning to recognize that the wisdom of our time must be more transitory and metamorphic than metaphoric, and that no principle is as much a cause of human social distress as "information lag," which I define as a discrepancy between what is now known and ultimately useable and what is actually practiced through much of the world.

Unfortunately the people who are responsible for the ultimate decisions and policies governing the actions of our people, and who also make the publicly observable decisions in our society, are not aware, for the most part, of this lag discrepancy. They are not aware of what is possible and what is feasible in a relatively short period of time. Buckminster Fuller has commented that this widespread information lag is at the root of the world's failure to solve its poverty although it is now possible to provide 100 per cent of current living humanity with the necessary material needs of life.

We must realize that the enemies of progress are those who hold vested interests in obsolete forms, and those who hold vested interests in obsolete practices, obsolete technology, and, most importantly, hold vested interests in archaic ideas. Perhaps the truth is all too obvious—that the greatest vested interest today is not property, but ignorance and the resulting inability to curtail the time between the conceptual presentation of an idea and the enactment of the utility of that idea for the benefit of a large segment of the human race.

To again quote Kostelanetz, "The fault of so much that is publicly presented in the press, and passes for radical thought in America today, is that it is really just a preoccupation with problems and remedies of an industrial malaise and supposed social inequity that concerned the prophets of a half century ago. In coping with the new realities and radical possibilities, I suggest that most of the ideas that we hear expressed by our lawmakers and our press belong less in our mind and more in our museums.

"We have a need to rethink how we will view radical change in this country, because the final third of this 20th century will be so fundamentally different than anything you or I have experienced, or our fathers have experienced, in the last 70 years—so fundamentally different and so radically different from anything that has ever been proposed by the radical left or the radical right. I think we must be less concerned and interested in what is now common experience, common conflict, or common agreement than in the discovery of uncommon possibilities."

The new possibilities and the new imaginations coming from technology will transgress anything we have heard or anything we have seen. They will literally stagger the human mind. The powers of these new technologies are so fundamental, yet so autonomous, that a particular crucial machine or device seems to have more or less the same effect on all individuals, on all environments, and on every culture that adopts it. As Kostelanetz states, "This similarity of effect, this history of shared technological awareness is probably the greatest ecumenical force in the world today."

Some people fear technology, failing primarily to recognize that it is a body of practice based upon a body of rational human knowledge constituted by rational human beings. Marshall McLuhan's dictum that there is no possible protection from technology except new technology, that the process of technology will save us from technology, and that to this process there is no limit or no end must be heeded. It is a situation with which we had better learn to live and I suggest we learn to enjoy. The ultimate enemy is not the new machine but a panoply of old ideas that keep us from using all the new machines, mechanisms, and devices as propitiously as we might for the benefit of all mankind. I know such ideas are not shared by some young people and by many individuals publicly expressing their views. I believe, however, there is little technological advance that we have seen in our lifetime that has not saved us from worse difficulties and miseries than the new technology has created.

There is far better correlation between the standard of living and the overall well-being of a society—with the degree to which the fruits of technology have been developed and distributed to that society—than one will find if one correlates social well-being with the form of government, or the nature of the political or economic system involved. The American corporation, the primary developer and distributor of the products and services evolving from technology, has performed its basic mission exceptionally well. It is the only wealth-creating organization in our society. All others are either wealth collecting, wealth distributing, or wealth destroying.

Being the primary vehicle by which technology is extended to social utility can, however, produce many attitudinal problems for the corporation. Technology and how it operates is simply not understood by the great majority of American citizens; it is certainly not understood by their governments. Perhaps we now understand why wealth creation processes, actually enacted to benefit all citizens, are so often ignored, feared, chastised, or penalized by our governmental activities.

The lack of appreciation of the nature of technology, its mission, and how it operates on the part of both government and the private citizen alike has greatly damaged the corporate image. The technology the public has been taught to fear is, of course, intimately associated with the activity of the corporation and, unfortunately, this association has had a marked negative effect on the corporate image.

We hear so much conversation and comment these days about pollution, the horrors of pollution and its effect on our life, on mankind, and on our cities. I remember a number of years ago standing in front of a statue in Vienna and witnessing the fact that in the thirteenth or fourteenth century, 80 percent of that city had died from the plague in a period of about fourteen months. Now that is pollution! Today, in our western industrial society, we have no such assaults by nature on mankind. To eliminate such difficulties as exemplified by the Vienna plague, it didn't require soothsayers, it didn't require critics of civilization, it didn't require critics of progress—it required an advancing scientific and medical profession. It required the lives of people like Pasteur and Koch. In this country, it required the growth of a very active and competent drug and medical industry. No one, if they rationally think about the matter, would prefer the worldwide biological pollution of yesterday to the urban chemical pollution of today. Such, however, is no excuse for technology not eliminating the latter, and I have little doubt such will be done. We should remember, however, that nature's pollutants—namely disease transmitted by mosquitoes—are still the largest cause of human pathology in the world.

We must recognize a few characteristic impacts of the new technology. One of the fruits of a technological society is the realization that the world's wealth is not a fixed quantity, and that technology is primarily responsible for a material abundance that allows America to tolerate one-fourth of its population as professional students. We must recognize the continuation of the growth of technology means the continuation of the growth of material and wealth equity for every man, woman and child. Science continually does more with less; wealth is created. This is contemporary magic. The study of natural laws, the subsequent organization of knowledge, and the subsequent application thereof, is the primary method by which the magic is accomplished. As Julian Huxley so vividly claims, "The creation of knowledge through the evolution of the human brain is the only inexhaustible resource with which man has to work." James Bryant Conant made the observation that the most significant progress comes not from the empirical fondling of old problems but from the opportunistic exploration of new concepts, new theories, new ideas and new information. The future results of our knowledge explosion are going to be most dramatic; we have already seen some evidences of its impact. As "the information lag" is shortened, we shall have an increase in leisure time for all, and poverty that politics can't cure will fall to the spoils of abundance. Although my Calvinistic ethic winces at the thought, I am sure the annual wage to everybody, whether they work or whether they don't, will be a reality within our lifetime. The development of new educational methods and teaching machines may radically change the entire learning process, and learning may well become the primary aim of life; education will be this country's largest industry and will promote a revolution within man himself; the reforming of society then will parallel the changes that occur within the individual. Science will not only have lifted burdens from men's backs; it will lift burdens from men's minds. This new society, geared to learning, will be able to absorb more of the inevitable continuing change, and be more resilient in accepting change than a society which is not so devoted to learning.

As technological progress proceeds and man shortens the lag period in which it is utilized, new value systems will occur. It shakes our convictions to realize that our value systems do not organize, restrict and direct technology; to a large degree, technological advance changes our value system. Our attitude toward sex, our attitude toward birth control and our attitude toward human behavior have probably been influenced more in the last ten years by "the pill" than by any other singular influence in the recent history of man. We can repeat analogous examples over and over again.

Technology, not government, has produced a generation that is more skeptical about war, more enthusiastic about the possibilities of machines, more tuned to computers, less desperate about accumulating wealth or conspicuous signs of wealth, more open to ideas, more tolerant of eccentricity, more committed to sweeping social change, less concerned about what it can get out of life, and more concerned about how it can make the system work.

A member of the press asked me, a number of weeks ago, who were the real leaders of society. He was a little bit annoyed, a bit chagrined and surprised when I didn't mention the Kennedys or the Rockefellers. I think the people who are really leading this society in the direction it is going are selected people that most of society never hear about. I can remember the day John Von Neumann died; there appeared a little sentence in my local paper, way down in a corner, "John

Von Neumann, Princeton, New Jersey, Eminent Mathematician, died today." I don't think there is any doubt about the fact that John Von Neumann has, or will at least, influenced the lives of more people in this room than any politician we have in office. Eugene Wigner, whom you don't recognize unless you are familiar with the world of physics and physicists, has probably influenced more scientists and technologists, who in turn, have influenced the growth of more areas of technology, than anyone now alive.

One particular gentleman, working in a university many years ago, said, "The practical man assumes that he is not influenced by the world of abstract ideas, but in reality, the practical man is influenced by nothing else but the world of abstract ideas." Unfortunately, the idea usually occurs twenty-five years before the so-called practical man is influenced by it. The man who made this statement was John Maynard Keynes. Most "practical men" in our society (and particularly our politicians) are tossed back and forth by the economics which Keynes professed during this time.

One individual you may wish to watch; he may be the Pasteur of our current generation of social ills. I refer to Jay Forrester of the Massachusetts Institute of Technology. His writings on social organizations and methods of programming them for mankind's benefit are beginning to dramatically influence the way we look at our social institutions. His classic article on the "Counterintuitive Nature of Social Organizations" has shocked many politicians and "do-gooders"; Jay Forrester contends, as the result of his "systems technology" study of social organizations, that many of the things that we do intuitively to solve our social problems will actually make them worse.

The people who "lead" our world of innovative thought have a number of characteristics; they have a power to initiate thought concept, and subsequently direct their attention to unexpected possibilities; they have the power to plan, and as Peter Drucker said "strategic planning is the vehicle by which information lags are shortened and put to work for the benefit of mankind."

Herman Kahn has stated, "Planning must be suprapolitical because the use of technology, for the benefit of society, by utilizing a planning methodology, is something governments cannot do. Governments are not currently staffed with the kind of people who even understand the concepts of long-range strategic planning. All that such individuals can usually do is respond to the day-by-day crises. Most of the real planning will have to be done by industry, by the universities, by nonprofit organizations, and even by individuals themselves." Buckminster Fuller has said that "to ask a politician to lead us is like asking the tail of a dog to lead the dog."

Most social and political revisionists talk, of course, about changing our system. These people fail to realize that our system is changing continually under the influence and pressure of ideas and technology. Most transformations occur outside the world of politics, which in today's world is really less of an initiating force than an adjusting operation basically providing regulations to cope with the changes that have or are already occurring.

Unfortunately, government's influence can perhaps only be one of restricting natural progress rather than progressively assisting the application of knowledge to human and social advancement. The less knowledgeable a political regime is, the less aware it is of new knowledge and technology, the more reactionary, the more laggard it becomes and the more irrelevant are its politics. It is, of course, unfortunately effective in extending the period during which the citizens ultimately achieve their inevitable future; perhaps all we can really do is reduce to a minimum this ability of government to increase "information lag".

Unfortunately, as Thomas Hughes wrote a few years ago, at least half seriously, "One can say that the 20th century is currently made up of 14th century farmers, 15th century theologians, 16th century politicians, 17th century economists, 18th century bureaucrats, 19th century generals, and 21st century scientists." Walter Wriston has since added, "It's not a bad analysis save for the American farmer, who belongs in the 20th century."

Our technological traditions are shaping a new thought, a "change ethic," as Donald Schon calls it, and its exponents do not descend from any common intellectual base. Peter Drucker, a conservative, speaks of a radically different future. Zbigniew Brzezinski, the violent anti-Communist, now says that communism is less of a threat to the United States than ideas that are out-of-date.

The new technology is nonutopian, nonideological; it doesn't offer final definitions but imaginative suggestions. It offers mind-expanding paths rather than mind-limiting walls. It is based on the notion that the more progress we make, the more we will have to make.

Dramatic changes in our society, enacted by technological progress, are going to happen within the next thirty years and we, as citizens, can either decide that we are going to be annoyed by it, destroyed by it, or enjoy it.

Most of us in management realize that if we are going to plan and manage an organization, if we are going to plan and manage the opportunities, if we are going to plan and manage events, and not be managed by them, we must have a conceptual awareness that transcends the events of today. We must be able to place the things that are going around us at the moment in a more extended time frame. We must be aware of the knowledge base and technology that is influencing the organization, indeed governing the organization that we are attempting to manage. The most vital quality of leadership today is the ability of a man who is running an operation to have a clear concept of "what the future could be like" in view of the technologies that dominate his organization. This ability is indeed that necessary motivating and charismatic quality that Berlew depicts as most significant, and must be added to the managerial posture and training pursued by our business schools.

In a society in which 60 percent of the Congress comes from a profession that is geared primarily to gauge what is appropriate today essentially in terms of what was useful yesterday, namely the legal profession, it is of no wonder that such people, when placed in jobs, either in the administrative or legislative components of our government, are finding it increasingly impossible to feel comfortable, to feel self-assured, to feel confident, that they can plan or influence the future of this country by the correct selection of conceptual conviction, by the appropriate level of conceptual legislation, by the right degree of conceptual decision.

Most of us fail to realize that a lawyer is able, by his training, to do only two things, important as they may be. He is able to draft a regulation or a law after somebody with expertise in some knowledgeable area has designated what particular conceptual horizon should be expressed. He is also, of course, able to investigate, prosecute, defend, or judge a situation in view of establishing regulations or existing law.

By training, he is not prepared to handle the varied conceptual trends and the conceptual realities in a wide spectrum of human knowledge or experience.

During the Nixon administration, but certainly not limited thereto, we witnessed most decision-making functions carried out by groups of people who represent a profession to whom technology, in its broad concept and character, is an unknown and an awesome thing.

One of the more specific yet dramatic examples of the ridiculous character of the decision processes currently emanating from our governmental personnel is the OSHA requirement that places phenyl d-naphthylamine and phenyl 3-naphthylamine under the same toxicity regulation. Any student of introductory organic chemistry would recognize the specified rules as unnecessary for one of these compounds and totally inadequate for the other. Today, most industrial technologists regularly encounter no end of similar legal absurdities.

Another example of the antiquity of governmental thought process is the perpetual fear of monopolistic control of product and market conditions, and the continuous desire to resurrect and reapply worn-out and now inapplicable antitrust laws and regulations. These laws were probably useful fifty or one hundred years ago, but have relatively little utility in a world economic and market situation where technological innovation long ago replaced domestic competition as the most significant factor influencing American trade capability in the international market. Our legislators should spend their time devising ways of encouraging research, development, and the necessary rewarding by patent protection for the innovative individual and corporation, regardless of the organization size, instead of retaining the antitrust battle cries of the nineteenth century. Why can't we develop such thought in government so necessary in our modern age? Ray Cromley, the columnist, stated in a recent editorial, "Two forces have combined to produce the overall unhappy condition of research and innovation in the United States. The first problem lies in our colleges and universities, traditionally the home of daring explorations. Here, the growing rigidity of the tenure system serves to block out the young, unknown scientist with new ideas. And the requirement that men publish regularly or perish, drives many into research in safe, popular areas where small reportable gains are easy to come by.

"The second major force stultifying our scientific and technological advance is the growing suspicion of basic and far-out research among members of Congress and the past several administrations. So great is the urge for immediate practical results that the government regularly shorts the future for possible immediate benefits. There is among the present Senate leadership an almost Neanderthal-like suspicion of basic science as a form of witchcraft.

"To make matters worse, the patent system, as now operated, intensifies the problems faced by inventors. Hardest hit is the small, high technology firm, where historically many major breakthroughs have been made. The patent process has become long, costly and quite uncertain. There is little evidence the inventor will be protected, once given a patent, even if he has the funds, which most don't, to engage in lengthy, expensive lawsuits.

"As is indicated above, the trend these days in government, in the universities and industry, is toward betting on sure things in research. We want quick, certain results.

"What makes the situation more ridiculous is that far-out research is relatively cheap, considering the high payoff when an idea pans out."

I might note a comment expressed thirty years ago by Irving Langmuir, "The most formidable threat to American research and innovation is the growing number of executives and politicians, who are making decisions affecting research policy and expenditure, whose training and experience does not permit them to know what it is all about."

If you move around Washington with any degree of frequency, you will rapidly become aware of the relative ignorance on the part of most of our elected and appointed representatives regarding this technological world in which we live. Most of them are trained in a manner which suggests that to see around the next corner, they should study the rearview mirror. They are trained in a profession which is oriented toward traditions and adversarial role playing. They are reactive to problems, not proactive to opportunities. They are concerned primarily about the concepts that were appropriate or existent twenty (or even one hundred) years ago, not about what new concepts have been born that now appear radically opportunistic.

If our nation is to be opportunistically in tune with the changes that are inevitable, if it is to predicate by effective planning and management the use of new technology rather than being injured by it, we must in some way generate the ability, without our governments, to handle the new information that lies before us. Indeed, I believe we must change the professional composition of our legislative and administrative government.

There are many reasons for the perpetuation of the high number of legally trained people in legislative and administrative government circles. Sydney Harris, the syndicated columnist, wrote in January of 1975, "Speaking of politics, as I was the other day (and as I do rarely), it seems to me that one of the most important restructurings we might make in our political machinery would be to change the 'reward system' for successful candidates for office.

"As American politics operates now, public offices tend to attract mostly lawyers; both houses of Congress and most state and local offices are heavily dominated by the legal profession. Law and government, after all, seem to go hand in hand, and the lawyer has a kind of professional expertise in such matters.

"Most of all, public office is rewarding to the lawyer per se, and nonrewarding to the nonlawyer. The lawyer in government can make a lot of money on the side, both legally and extra-legally, for himself, for the firm he has left, or for the firm he contemplates joining as soon as he leaves public office.

"Almost everything involved in government has its legal-financial aspect, which the lawyer-official can turn to his advantage: contracts, leases, construction, taxes, insurance, environment, you name it. A lawyer doesn't have to steal in office, he just has to be moderately clever and enterprising, and he can get rich.

"But, while politics is 'positively reinforcing' for the lawyer to enter, it is 'negatively reinforcing' for the nonlawyer. Whatever else his profession or occupation, public office involves a sacrifice. He has to give up what he has always made a living at, often for a smaller income, and with little opportunity to compensate or recoup.

"Out of the legal stream, the nonlawyer finds the important committees and agencies dominated by lawyers, while he possesses no leverage for making deals, siphoning business to his old firm, or devising corporate entities that will enrich him when he leaves public life.

"The nonlawyer in politics is often sacrificing his financial future;

the lawyer is augmenting his. The nonlawyer who has been successful must take a cut in his living standard (unless he has an independent income) when he enters office; the lawyer looks upon office-holding as one of the quickest and surest ways to raise his living standard, if that is what he wants (and that is often what he wants).

"Representatives should be representative of the whole spectrum of society; our founders, the signers of the Constitution, were mostly farmers with some merchants, lawyers and artisans. We were not designed to be a government dominated by one breed, and it is time we devised a reward system to encourage and sustain other kinds of men in office."

The Watergate situation of past months exemplifies a situation wherein people were placed in responsible jobs for which they had no conceptual ability, and in which they had absolutely no innate feeling of competency. Individuals from industry know what happens when such occurs. One of three things happens: individuals so placed may, of course, realize with honesty they don't have it; they can't "cut the mustard"; they quit. Secondly, they may, of course, go off to a corner and hide, hoping that nobody places them in a position where they have to make a decision. Finally, if the individual has a strong ego and other augmenting emotional characteristics, he may begin to change the laws of the game. He begins to play the game of politics; he begins to play the game of power. A new self-assumed "role" replaces his legitimate and expected functional performance. A man with a strong ego, who has no sense of competency in the area of knowledge that he is supposed to lead, certainly has this alternative if he is to opiate that ego; unconsciously or deliberately, he can play the power game. Such is what happened to certain members of the Nixon administration.

Although their actions may be characterized by more legality, many members of Congress are also succumbing to the same "role replacement of legitimate function"; they are delighted with the opportunity to investigate, prosecute (or defend) and judge the executive branch of government. They are now "doing their thing." The CIA affair has now replaced Watergate. The challenge of strategic conceptual planning, if they ever recognize the need for same (and the legislative formulation resulting therefrom), never caused them anything but frustration.

"Watergate-like" events will happen again and again if we don't succeed in placing people in government with the knowledge and conceptual ability so necessary for enacting the vision and the planning functions so necessary in our changing technological world.

We can no longer afford decisions by politicians who have no conceptual ability, no relevant training or experience, and no innate feeling of competence to deal with the complex issues inherent in our modern society. Any such individual, even if he escapes the illegal acts of a Watergate, can, when he utters judgment and decisions in matters wherein he possesses no significant understanding, certainly at least be guilty of the "arrogance of ignorance." Let me outline my idea of the role of governments in the area of strategic planning. I believe most American organizations, the federal government and the American corporation included, are now overmanaged, overstaffed, and underled. We do not need tactical economic and production planning, as many government individuals and agencies now suggest (most of them have little concept of the real character of the planning process); such has done little for England or for the Soviet Union. A relatively free market, motivated by technological advance and the exploitation of technology by the American corporation, has done more for the average American citizen than any other socioeconomic system contrived by man has done for anyone. We do not need more tactical management by the federal government; we need more strategic leadership. How can this best be done? First we need government representatives and administrators with sufficient knowledge of the new technologies to know "what the future could be." We do not now have many such people in our Washington electorate. Then we should enact a planning process best described by John Diebold within his poignant remarks to the French Ministry of Economics and Finance: "The dynamics of the market, and feedback control through profit—not corporate form or management techniques—make private business the most effective innovator and resource allocator man has ever invented. For society to benefit from this much needed ability to fulfill human needs, it is the social responsibility of business to pursue profit. The task of government is to establish incentives and constraints in such a way that profit is made doing what society most needs done, in a manner society finds acceptable."

The progress of this country must be influenced by people with knowledge; it must be influenced by the people who understand the basic technological concepts that can lead us to the fulfillment of the opportunities that confront this country; I hope that in some way we can, in the future, find a way to place increased numbers of technically oriented people and scientifically trained individuals, also possessing leadership and managerial aptitudes, in both the administrative and legislative areas of our government. If we do not find a vehicle for so involving such individuals in our governmental decision process, the described information lag will become so extreme and debilitating that our society will certainly suffer.

Dr. Ralph E. Lapp, in a recent partially humorous but very significant paper, "Should the President Be a Nobel Prize Winner," offers the following comment:

"Why aren't more scientists and engineers serving as senators and representatives in Congress, as governors, state legislators and judges?

"The question is not an idle one because we live in a highly technological society. The big problems facing this society—energy, pollution, urban blight, arms control, population—are largely scientific/technical ones, yet the decisions relative to their solutions are being made by scientific amateurs if not ignoramuses.

"It may be argued that these big problems are more than just scientific, that they are also human and moral problems. This is true, but no special group or profession has an exclusive corner on humanity and morality (not even the clergy), and the individuals who have governed the world for the last 5,000 years (priests, princes, soldiers, kings, popes, lawyers, landowners, capitalists and commissars) have shown no great special ability and only a minimum of 'morality' and humanity. Perhaps it is time to let a few of the professionally trained in the most rigorous disciplines of the mind, plus the most relevant area of study, into the decision making organizations of government, not just advisory boards and committees, because advice (which can be easily ignored) is not the same as power.

"Science has so drawn the world together and so rapidly remolded civilization that the social structure is now strained at many points. . . . Though our civilization is based on science, the scientific method has little place in the making of our laws. . . . We see in the ranks of science knowledge without power and in politics power without knowledge. Relative to this observation, it is interesting to note that scientists 'discover' laws that are true, engineers 'apply' scientific laws to make things work, but politicians 'pass' laws which regulate but may neither work nor be true.

"Differences between individuals, corporations, special groups, etc., must be settled in an adversary, legal manner (if we are not to return to trial by combat), but can the big environmental, energy, population problems be effectively dealt with through this procedure? At present, the nation's nuclear power plant building program—the only viable solution to the energy problem in the near future—is years behind schedule due to hundreds of lawsuits brought by pressure groups who represent small minorities (and a variety of technical competence), not the majority.

"Congress, of course, passes laws designed to solve these big national problems; and even if it were a Congress of technocrats, individuals or groups could challenge the constitutionality of their laws as they do at present. But if 50 per cent of the members of Congress were scientists, perhaps their recommendations on scientific-technical matters would command more respect and less litigation. What our society needs today is fewer lawsuits and more cooperation, more engineered solutions and fewer legal roadblocks."

In the same vein, Theodore Roszak has recently written, "In a technocracy, nothing is any longer small or simple or readily apparent to the nontechnical man. Instead, the scale and intricacy of human activities—political, economic, cultural—transcends the competence of the amateurish citizen and inexorably demands the attention of specially trained experts—everything aspires to become purely technical, the subject of professional attention. The technocracy is therefore the regime of experts—or of those who employ experts.

"But a rule of 'experts' is not democratic rule. Not everybody qualifies, only those competent, educated and certified. This conflicts with the traditional American viewpoint that the common man with his fund of common sense can cope with any problem, any crisis and fill any government post. The Founding Fathers did not have exactly this point of view. They limited the right to hold office and vote while writing checks and balances into the Constitution. But after President Andrew Jackson, and more recently the civil rights movement (one man–one vote) the idea that every citizen—male or female, white, black or brown—was qualified to hold any public office, became common.

"When life in the Republic was more simple, when most men were farmers, mechanics (carpenters, coopers, blacksmiths), trappers, hunters, or miners, it was probably true that given average intelligence, the common man could effectively perform the requirements of any political office. His fund of experience encompassed all the major problems of his time. He and his peers were self-reliant equals growing their own food, building their own homes, providing their own transportation (afoot or horseback) and their own national defense (the rifle over the fireplace). They were an independent people as the remark of the Irishman, 'I'm as good as you are, and a great deal better too,' shows.

"This independence led to a democratic faith which held that no special group could mediate between the common man and the truth in political matters, even though trained competence might make the difference between success and disaster.

"The observation is often made, 'If we can put men on the moon, why can't we solve our problems of the cities: poverty, pollution, population and energy?' One answer is that there are two distinct and separate 'we's' referred to. The 'we' that put men on the moon were highly trained, competent scientists, engineers and astronauts. The 'we' that has been in charge of the poverty and urban problems are a completely different group with an entirely different form of education, training and experience.

"As a result of this miscasting of characters, plus the real problems resulting from industrial 'future shock', technology is now on trial. Many people have concluded that scientists have committed more sins against society than they have provided benefits. The scientific revolution as applied through technology and industry, looms so large in the public mind that people make the false assumption that scientists are in control.

"There is, however, a positive benefit of the technoscience revolution that too few have spoken about. This is the phenomenal growth of knowledge. Collectively, we know more than any people at any time in history. And knowledge is power. Therefore, as the United States depletes its natural resources stored for millions of years beneath the ground, it has the option of using its even more valuable natural resource located about five feet above the ground, the accumulated brainpower of a technologically advanced society."

The challenge before the American people is specific and clear: how does this country replace, in its legislative and administrative structure, the large number of politically oriented amateurs, operating without benefit of significant training or experience in a varied spectrum of human knowledge, with an appropriate density of human brainpower, capable of turning problems into opportunity, knowledge into progress—and more importantly—insuring national survival.

Note: The writer wishes to acknowledge the frequent use of the writings of Richard Kostelanetz—primarily *Beyond Left and Right*—in the preparation of this paper.

FIVE

Some Realistic Views regarding the Social Responsibility of Business

In this paper on the corporation's involvement in its community, Don M. Alstadt asserts that the corporation's primary responsibility is to contribute to the community's well-being through employment and generation of profit.

"I would challenge the American corporation to resist the acceptance of every community task that some do-gooder or promoter would force upon it because consciously or unconsciously the community feels the corporation can 'get things done.' Instead I suggest the corporation should say, 'Let us teach you how to manage, to motivate, to plan, to strategize, to execute, to control!'"
—DON M. ALSTADT

During the past several years, we have witnessed a growing demand on the leaders of our corporations and businesses to solve, or to support financially, the solutions of many economic and social problems currently inherent in our society. The gauntlet of demands has included requests that business concentrate on the preferential promoting of minority group employees, extending credit freely in slums, selling

Speech given circa 1970.

food to the poor at below-market prices, assuming the major portion of the responsibility for environmental rehabilitation, etc.

George Stigler, Walgreen Professor of American Institutions at the University of Chicago, has stated, in his most comprehensive paper "Modern Man and His Corporation," that these demands (plus the subsequent willingness of many corporations and executives to over-exercise both their consciences and their efforts) have given both society and the corporation "a much inflated view of corporate power and influence. . . . Our repeated petitions to business leaders to solve our problems," states Professor Stigler, "is giving them an illusion of power which they do not possess. . . . In a good economic system, and ours is a superb economy, individual businesses can do very little good, and therefore very little harm, and that is as it should be. . . . Let us not seek to transform the greatest economy in all history into a third class welfare agency."

There are few critics in our society who, after significant rational thought, would willingly and permanently transpose themselves to any other economic or social environment, in another place or time period. The American economy has provided a higher standard of living for a higher percentage of its population than any other in history. Americans on the supposed "bottom of the economic totem pole" live better than the majority of the earth's citizenry.

Certainly we have social and economic problems, but technology and the American productive enterprise have solved far more destructive and serious problems than they have created or we now possess. What current pollution difficulty compares with the pollution of the cities of Europe and America by infectious diseases during past centuries? When have we seen 80 percent of a city's population die in twelve months from "pollution"; such did happen in Vienna at the height of the Plague. Vienna's problems, and many others like them, were not solved by loud critics of civilization, but by a few individuals, Lister, Pasteur, Koch, etc., whose vision and understanding far exceeded that of the crowd—and by the subsequent productive capability of the health industries that produce vaccines, antiseptics, and drugs.

Technology and industry have produced few problems by their actions that did not eliminate other problems, suffering, and inconvenience more serious than those newly created. The American corporation certainly has given the American society more than it has taken from it. The American business enterprise is the only producer of tangible wealth in our economy; all other organizations are wealth distributing or disseminating—and some organizations manage to destroy whatever equity they acquire.

What then is the rational social responsibility of the American corporation? I suggest that the corporation effectively exercises its social responsibility when it provides, to each of its *stakeholders,* an appropriate balance of return, goods, or services consistent with the corporation's mission, resources, and abilities. No corporation will long exist if its mission is inconsistent with all its stakeholders' needs. Also, no corporation will long exist if it is required to provide any one stakeholder group with all the "components of happiness" that one stakeholder might demand. The remaining stakeholders will surely put the organization out of business and the community as a whole may subsequently suffer.

Who are these stakeholders? They are, I suggest, the customers, the employees, the stockholders, the suppliers, the creditors, and the communities in which the corporation operates. All of these individual groups are units of society to be served by the corporation; no one group can make unreasonable demands on the assets or abilities of the organization if the corporation is to fulfill its primary economic function—the continuous creation of economic wealth and equity.

When the corporation subtracts its expenses from its income, it certainly hopes it has a profit remaining. Approximately half of this profit is immediately taken in taxes. From the remaining "half-profit" a minor portion is given to the stockholders, as dividend payment for risk taking, and the remainder of the "half-profit" is reinvested in the business as land, buildings, equipment, etc., to enable a continuation of the production, increase in employment, and increase of the community's total economic wealth. Without this reinvestment and continuous production of equity, the corporation would soon cease to exist. This remaining "half-profit" that the American corporation keeps must be used for the benefit of all its stakeholders or our only social wealth and equity creating process ceases.

Perhaps a special comment regarding one of the corporation's stakeholders, the community in which the corporation operates, would be in order. The corporation, of course, has certain responsibilities to the community as it has to other stakeholders—the most basic of which is the continuous operation of an economically viable and productive corporate enterprise.

The corporate president who serves unselfishly on many community social services boards and projects, and because of lack of time or motivation doesn't promote the full economic wealth-creating capabilities of the corporate enterprise, is not fulfilling his primary community responsibility. The corporation that seemingly supports every community social service and fund-raising program, but that does not have the vision, courage, and drive to develop the technology, products, and foreign markets that will promote the nation's economic balance of payments, is likewise not utilizing its resources in the unique manner that only the industrial corporation can evidence. The community in which the corporation operates, plus all the other stakeholders, will eventually suffer from neglect of this corporate primary mission and "a priori" social responsibility.

We must again emphasize that one half of the corporation's profit is taken in taxes before the corporation can exercise any discretion regarding the distribution of the remainder as dividends, reinvestment in plant, facilities, etc. Certainly a large share of the corporation's tax contribution is subsequently used by society for welfare and social rehabilitation; this fact is too often forgotten by community and program fund-raisers. Direct discretionary financial support, by the corporation, of social and community efforts should, I believe, be limited to those contributions in time or money that would aid the stakeholders to continuously advance the corporation's primary social and community capability—the economic and wealth-producing capability of the organization.

I believe there are three community activities toward which the industrial corporation might therefore evidence direct auxiliary support. If an employee or any other stakeholder has (1) health and (2) knowledge, he certainly should be able to "make it" in our society, unless he is limited by lack of motivation or ambition. The corporate support of (1) hospitals and selected health service organizations, and (2) selected institutions of learning, education, and training would therefore appear to be very logical and justifiable from the viewpoint of any stakeholder. If our American corporation is to effectively compete in world markets, it must do so with high technology products and with highly innovative managerial and marketing methods. Few organizations in our society may, in the future, be as vital to the American business enterprise as the private academic institution of higher learning. With its relatively greater freedom of innovation and flexibility in our changing world, the private university is vital as an influence in the honing of the corporation's "cutting edge." If and when, however, our health care and educational enterprises are entirely dominated by tax support (I certainly don't look favorably on this possibility), corporate discretionary support of such community activity should, I believe, be terminated; our tax burden for such domination would be even more demanding than it is at present. The third community activity that corporations should expect to support, far more than they do, is those organizations who themselves promote and attempt to protect the free corporate enterprise base that is the backbone of the American economy, organizations that attempt to educate the public and government representatives (many of whom possess greatly distorted notions regarding the mission and character of the American business) are, I believe, vital to the continued growth of our only entity that produces tangible economic wealth for all—the American corporation or business.

I do not believe it is the responsibility of the American corporation or business to contribute to every cause and produce a system, as George Stigler comments, that will "make life sure and sweet—and provide man with all the manufacturable components of happiness." I'm sure Professor Stigler is referring to the direct underwriting of all man's wants—not to the effective satisfaction of need that results from the formation and maintenance of a healthy economy. The latter is certainly a definite corporate responsibility. I also do not believe that all community fund-raising activities or problem-solving ventures should focalize their efforts at the corporate and business world; community leaders will, of course, often state that business has the capabilities to organize and "get things done." But business has its own unique mission and economic and social responsibility to the community to "get done" and if such does not occur, the economic fiber of the community will surely collapse.

Perhaps we should recognize what is meant when society says business can "get things done." One does not have to accept or agree with the objectives or mission of the corporate business to recognize that of all the institutions in our society, the corporation achieves and fulfills a higher percentage of its goals than any other segment. We will freely admit that, in the execution of future corporate objectives, consideration must be given to factors that were given inadequate consideration in the past—environmental control, health standards characterizing working conditions, etc. Such responsibility, however, should certainly be limited to action within the corporate structure and operation, and be vital considerations inherent in the methods by which the corporation manages its affairs. Such should not be indicative of the corporation's assuming responsibility for components of society over which it has no authority or control.

The American corporation simply manages its manpower and resources with far more competent and effective motivations, planning, execution, and control than do society's other organizational units. It is difficult for many of us, who daily see gross imperfections in our management capabilities, to recognize that regardless of such imperfections, the corporation is thirty or forty years ahead of government, most educational institutions, charitable organizations, etc., in the application of leadership and motivational management techniques. The profit motive, and perhaps others, has certainly forced, as the psychiatrist Dershiemer has stated, the American corporation to become the most "realistic environment" in our society and made necessary the elimination of much self-delusion that contributes to ineffective management of people and resources.

Indeed, as John Diebold in his superb address before the French Ministry of Economics, states, "The dynamics of the market, and feedback control through profit—not primarily corporate form or management techniques—make private business the most effective innovator and resource allocator man has ever invented. For society to benefit from this much needed ability to fulfill human needs, it is the social responsibility of business to pursue profit. The task of government is to establish incentives and constraints in such a way that profit is made doing what society most needs done, in a manner society finds acceptable."

I would challenge the American corporation to resist the acceptance of every community task that some do-gooder or promoter would force upon it because, consciously or unconsciously, the community feels the corporation can "get things done." Instead I suggest that the corporation should say, "Let us teach you how to manage, to motivate, to plan, to strategize, to execute, to control! We will share our techniques and methodologies with you! If we teach you to fish rather than give you food," to paraphrase a Chinese proverb, "you will be able to provide for your lifetime." The reactive, "adversary-base orientation" of decision making in our governmental structure—so inherent within the legally trained mind—certainly must be replaced by conceptual planning—with its emphasis on purpose, objectives, participative techniques, and opportunity (as contrasted to problem) outlook—if society and government are to lift themselves from their confusion and frustration.

I would also suggest that the corporations, or individuals for that matter, withhold financial support from community organizations that are obviously poorly managed. A "good cause" or idea promoted by ineffective leadership and management does not usually suggest or produce useful results—and no executive would rationally invest in such a combination in his own business. Such a policy would demand that the corporation be most judicious in the selection of those external community programs and individuals meriting its support. Should such not be expected of good corporate management?

Only when all of society's institutions can effectively manage their resources will the social and economic well-being of the community be effectively served. To see that this management capability is widely created may indeed be, after the creation of community economic wealth, the most significant social responsibility of business.

Economic Education: What Should We Learn about the Free Market?

Six Recommendations for Students of Economics

I must admit at the outset that I am not an economist. I am a physical scientist whose passion is the thermodynamics of the "solid state," that is, matter that is neither liquid nor gas and that makes up the surfaces of nearly everything that is in the world. It is a complex, enigmatic, and fascinating subject—one that once prompted the great physicist Wolfgang Pauli to comment that although God created the universe, the Devil surely must have created its surfaces.

Recommendation 1: Study the Creation of Knowledge

But perhaps such a comment applies equally to economics; after all, economists deal with the surfaces of the marketplace. And the economy that results from human action is a "world" that is so complex, enigmatic, and fascinating that it might well be a divine—or devilish—creation. But the similarities between economics and physics don't end there. I believe we may learn a great deal about eco-

Speech given for the Ludwig von Mises Lecture Series, 1994, Hillsdale College, Hillsdale, Mich.

nomics by studying what has happened to sciences like physics and chemistry.

This is because economics is a comparatively "young science." Although Plato and Aristotle wrote of the importance of labor and commerce over two thousand years ago, it was not until the eighteenth century that philosophers like David Hume, Adam Smith, and David Ricardo devoted serious attention to the study of the marketplace. Thus, it is only logical to conclude that some of this science's most important truths—its great discoveries, its increased levels of understanding—still lie before us. For modern students of economics, this is exciting rather than disheartening news: They have the opportunity not only to fulfill their curiosity and their intellectual potential but to be pioneers in the creation of knowledge. These are opportunities, moreover, that their counterparts in the hard sciences have had and continue to have.

In this context, Niels Bohr, the founder of modern physics, once noted that in the search for knowledge there are two kinds of truth: There are "big truths," the opposite of which may also be true, and there are "little truths," the opposite of which are false. It is the "big truths" that are especially important in deciding controversial questions. For years the scientific community was divided over the question of whether light was a wave—a form of energy, as was predicated by wave theorists—or whether it was a particle, as dictated by Newtonian mechanics. Which answer was correct? A French philosopher and physicist, Prince Louis Victor de Broglie, advanced a very simple equation demonstrating that *both* answers were correct; he understood a "big truth" that nobody had considered before.

Jons Berzelius, the famous Swedish chemist, was widely assumed to know everything in the world that there was to know about chemistry in the mid-nineteenth century. The only question in doubt was whether there would ever be anyone like him again. Then came not one, but a number of discoveries, mainly by German chemists, which brought some new "big truths" to light and which proved once again that knowledge is not static: It is constantly expanding. The scientists who followed Berzelius dramatically changed the nature of chemistry because they were *synthesizing*, instead of merely analyzing ideas. And because of their efforts, a totally new field—organic chemistry—was born.

Likewise, in 1880, the conventional wisdom was that all the important questions in physics had been answered. Then, in the course of his research on thermodynamics, the German physicist Max Planck discovered modern quantum mechanics, which revolutionized all of physics. Biology also saw great changes in the 1930s–40s, though most biologists had no idea of what lay in store for them, namely, in the field of molecular biology. The point is, no one can predict what new knowledge will be created in any science, whether it be in physics, chemistry, biology—or economics.

Recommendation 2: Study the Creation of Wealth

In economics, one of the first intellectual pioneers was an individual I have already mentioned: the Scottish philosopher Adam Smith. An eyewitness to the tremendous prosperity caused by the Industrial Revolution, Smith argued that wealth was not some "pie" to be divided by the richest members of society but that it was constantly expanding and that it was something every class could strive to create and from which they could all benefit. He formally introduced this profound idea in his monumental study of the economy, *An Inquiry into the Nature and Causes of the Wealth of Nations* in 1776. I am in a position to appreciate Smith's message about wealth, because I have been one of those fortunate individuals who have enjoyed a great degree of economic success. One of my patents has resulted to date in $2.5–$3 billion in sales and almost $800 million in net profits. I do not mention this in order to boast but to document, through my own experience, the fact that there is no limit to the creation of wealth.

The best precondition for the creation of wealth, Smith knew, is a free market. In a free market, men are able to compete, but that is not really the lifeblood of the economy. Cooperation is. Sadly, few economists really study cooperation. Too many have accepted the liberal/socialist myth that capitalism is all about exploitation and self-interest instead of what Smith called "fellow feeling." Yet the time will surely come when economists undergo the same sort of change in attitudes that is taking place in other disciplines. For example, Robert Augros and George Stanciu, the former a philosopher and the latter a physicist, have in their book *The New Biology* seriously questioned the Darwinian concept that in nature all organic beings are exposed to severe competition and to the universal struggle for life, a paradigm that has dominated biology for over a century. In fact, many biologists now believe that competition is not as common as assumed, that nature employs many strategies to avoid competition, that cooperation, or what they call "synergism," is far more common, and that competition often is only a transitory phase leading to cooperation. In other words, the conventional wisdom that the "survival of the fittest" is the most important biological law is quickly being supplanted by a newly discovered "big truth."

Recommendation 3: Study the "Work Ethic"

Over the last several years, I have taken notes during our major political elections whenever I hear the candidates utter eight specific terms: "Rights" appeared 135 times; "freedom," 2,700; "jobs," 2,100; "job opportunity" 2,100; "fun and enjoyment," 2,300; "responsibility," 78; "self discipline," 77; "work," 140; and "duty," 3. The last four terms, which constitute what may be called the "work ethic," are obviously rusty from disuse.

I recommend that students concentrate less on the abstract theories that tend to dominate economic research and more on the nature of the work ethic. They should learn what incentives men have to succeed, and why some men follow through on them and others do not. Nobel Prize–winning economist James Buchanan agrees, stating, "Any economic theory that does not involve a considerable dependence on the work ethic is not useful." Why? Because work is key to understanding human economic behavior as well as human well-being (i.e., happiness, satisfaction, and self-esteem). According to Buchanan, the basic personal desire to work is deeply embedded in the human psyche. It is not just a vehicle of survival, and it does implicitly contribute a value-added dimension to our economic growth. It also represents a true economic force in the wealth-creation process—a process that produces a spillover benefit for all. Such force and effect, Buchanan concludes, may be neutralized by the "leisure-time" syndrome growing in our society. The basic psychological will to work is, therefore, a vital component of any future economic theory.

And there are all sorts of theories from which to choose—like "flow theory," which deals with the impact of information on the human mind, to "systems dynamics," which focuses on the impact of human organization on the corporation. For those students who are really interested, there is also "complexity theory," "chaos theory," and "game theory," all of which may have application to economic behavior.

Recommendation 4: Study the Corporation

Another interesting and little understood economic question is this: "What is the purpose of the corporation?" Not long ago, I asked that question at the World Economic Forum, before an international audience of hundreds of business executives. I assumed that the forum members, especially those from the United States, would share some basic understanding of the purpose of the corporation. But what I discovered was that there is very little agreement, particularly among Americans, on this subject. Each businessman seems to have a different perception of why his corporation exists.

To me, however, the basic purpose of the corporation is very simple and easily understood. It is to move new and useful knowledge into the marketplace for the benefit of a wide range of stakeholders. The first stakeholder is, of course, the customer. Satisfying his wants and needs is fundamental. Company owners, investors, the community, the nation, stockholders, creditors—these are all stakeholders too, and satisfying them is also important.

Recommendation 5: Study Human Psychology, Risk Taking, and Leadership

Because it results in action, the human mind not only perceives but changes reality. What men think leads to what they do and who they know themselves to be. But this is a causal relationship that deserves far more serious examination by economists—Douglas Bond, the former dean of the Department of Psychiatry at Case Western Reserve University Medical School, stated many years ago that laws, expressed principles of economics, and other factors determining economic decisions must distinguish between human hopes, human wants, and human needs.

He noted, for instance, that one cannot not comprehend a situation in which the relationship between a buyer and a seller is not affected by such distinctions, saying, in effect, "with a mere want, I can keep my money in my pocket just as long as I feel like it, until I'm convinced that I've got the best deal. But with a need, I don't have control over the time element, so I won't always hold out." Bond thus reminds all students of economics that they should pay more attention to the effects of human psychology on the marketplace.

Another fascinating area of study is risk taking. When starting a corporation, a businessman must determine his limits: his financial capabilities, his legal responsibilities, his available manpower, etc. But he must also seek to broaden those limits while maximizing his opportunity at a risk level that is not necessarily "minimal" (which is what many experts will say is best) but "tolerable." Many experts also like to opine that the market comes first; the customers will tell you what they "want," but often the businessman must gamble and create a product in order to discover whether it will be in demand. It's not just "markets, management, and money" that make a corporation succeed. As the founder of the Lord Company said to me when I first joined his firm, "It's the *right* product for the market, the *right* people, and the *right* money." For all of these to come together, risk taking is essential.

And the right kind of risk taking comes from the right kind of leadership. By leadership, I don't mean just management. Management is doing what you are doing today and learning to do it better. Leadership is making sure that ten years from now you are doing the right thing. Leadership, unfortunately, is lacking in modern American industry. Our corporations are overmanaged and underled. We need more entrepreneurs with vision, with thoughts that transcend what other people may be thinking, with the passion, courage, and integrity to inspire others with the same qualities. Students of economics should not leave the study of leadership up to psychologists or others. Leadership should be among their paramount concerns.

Recommendation 6: Study Liberty

There is at least one other vital area of study for those interested in economics, and that is liberty. It is an area that concerns me particularly since, in addition to being a scientist, I am a businessman, the head of a chemical corporation that, with thousands of other corporations around the country, provides jobs, buys and sells a wide variety of products, benefits countless individuals' lives, and helps America prosper.

By "liberty," I do not mean "license"; instead I mean the kind of freedom with corresponding responsibilities that our founding fathers sought to protect. This kind of liberty has been under slow but steady assault. In recent decades, we have seen the huge negative impact of big government on individuals, corporations, and the economy. Over-regulation has inhibited our innovative spirit and has tended to encourage the worst rather than the best economic outcomes. Those who run corporations know this instinctively: A widespread presence of regulation results in the enervation of the organization, a transfer of movement from a proactive, opportunity-oriented mood to a reactive, risk-minimizing mood. Moreover, it discourages the creation of new knowledge, the willingness to accept responsibility, vision, and leadership.

Now I am not an advocate of total deregulation; there are regulations and government activities that are necessary. But far too many are not. Perhaps it is because too many of our politicians tend to think like lawyers. Indeed, many *are* lawyers; there currently are more lawyers in Congress than in any other governing body in the world. This observation should not be construed as an attack on the legal profession. For more than a decade I have served as the chairman of the board of a law school, and I firmly believe that the legal profession is an honorable one. But lawyers are trained in the "case system," not in the world of economics or business. Lawyers generally react to situations in a way that would indicate that they are able to do four things: They investigate, they defend, they prosecute, or they judge some particular event or situation in terms of an existing law or regulation. They think, in other words, like building inspectors. They don't think like architects.

I urge all students of economics to resist thinking like lawyers and building inspectors. They should think like architects and thus become students of liberty. They should not blindly look to pie-in-the-sky regulation to control human behavior; they should look to the firm realities of human nature and seek their answers there. And they should willingly and boldly explore all new and different ideas that may affect the marketplace. The game has just begun. The science of economics is bound to change and grow enormously over the next twenty, thirty, and forty years. It is anything but a "dismal science"; it is a young science, and that is what makes it exciting. If its students are curious, and if they are synergistic in their approach rather than strictly analytical, they may discover some important "big truths" and create new breakthroughs in economics as well as human understanding.

SEVEN

Myths We Live By

PRESIDENT SULLIVAN, Board of Trustees of Allegheny, parents, guests, recipients, graduating seniors, friends. About a year and a half ago, my wife, Judy, and I decided to return to one of our favorite haunts in the world, a little hotel on the western coast of Ireland called Renvyle House. Renvyle House has historically been a haven for people like Oscar Wilde, James Joyce, William Butler Yeats, and other Irish poetic figures. Our purpose for visiting Renvyle was to fish for sea trout. I had been promised by the owner that there probably wouldn't be any guests other than ourselves. We would have the streams in total solitude and everything would be very restful and wonderful. Unfortunately, when we arrived, we found that Richard Harris and his entourage had moved into the hotel to make the film *The Field*. Actors were occupying all my favorite fishing haunts with their equipment and decor; consequently, my fishing experience was terminated. Fortunately, however, Renvyle House has a library and because of its very poetic heritage the library had accumulated a great number of fascinating books. While perusing through this library, I came across a very impressive little poem written by William Butler Yeats:

Things fall apart; the center cannot hold;
Mere anarchy is loosed upon the world,

Speech given at the Allegheny College commencement, May 19, 1991.

The blood dimmed tide is loosed; and everywhere
The ceremony of innocence is drowned;
The best lack all conviction, while the worst
Are full of passionate intensity.
 (From "The Second Coming")

Somehow or another, those last two phrases, "the best lack all conviction" while "the worst are full of passionate intensity," are expressions
which tore at my soul and my conscience until I decided to select, in
my own way, my view of our society's misplaced passionate intensities.
Perhaps some are a form of myths which guide us, often, in an irrational but, to the majority, a seemingly logical fashion. In the last few
months, I have, therefore, collected a few beliefs that, in my mind, are
really myths that guide us and motivate us in questioning directions
as a society, whether it be in our corporate world, in our government
world, or in our educational institutions. I'm quite fortunate that I do
spend and have spent a considerable amount of time in the corporate
world, in the halls of government, which are, most of the time, very
frustrating and in the academic environment, which is usually more
inspiring. Let me deal with nine of these myths quickly. You can judge
whether or not you think they serve us as a nation and society. Maybe
some of them, even though they are myths, are those that we should
take seriously and more rigorously adopt. Others should be modified
or rejected.

Myth Number One

America was founded as a democracy at its inception—enthused about
the possibility of one man, one vote. I think that if one goes back
and reads the Constitution and Declaration of Independence, one
does not find the word *democracy* anywhere in these documents. The
word *republic* is paramount. I had this strange dilemma emphasized
to me about three months ago when I listened to Erwin Griswold,
dean emeritus of the Harvard Law School, confront some students at
Lafayette College after one of them said, "Dean, that is not consistent
with democracy." Well, in the next ten minutes, the young student was
rigorously educated by Dean Griswold as to the difference between
a republic and a democracy and, at least in Dean Griswold's mind,

(1) the merits of a republic as a governmental entity, and (2) the lack of enthusiasm our founding fathers had for Jacksonian democracy and its practice. I will say no more, but think about it.

Myth Number Two

Many scholars think that the United States' Constitution is a complete document, adequate for the support of present and future laws, economic regulations, and social behavior. There are some people in this country who think otherwise. As a matter of fact, former Governor Shafer of Pennsylvania is involved in a very dramatic and wonderful institution called the Freedom Foundation at Valley Forge, PA. One of its quests is to introduce into our government a Bill of Human Responsibility that would parallel our Bill of Rights. About two years ago I had Judge Bork in my office and I confronted Judge Bork, that scholar of the Constitution, with the advisability of having, within our Constitution, a Bill of Human Responsibility. Judge Bork thought that might be a laudable idea. But how does one do it? I'll leave that for you, the next generation, to enact. There are, incidentally, some fifteen or twenty states that have, through the Freedom Foundation's efforts, put forth such programming and supported the introduction of Bills of Human Responsibility in the constitutions of their states.

Myth Number Three

Our preoccupation as a society with the win-lose scenarios is entirely consistent with the optimum development of Homo sapiens into human beings. We are all fascinated by win-lose scenarios. We love football games, we love athletic events. But I'm reminded of a comment by Pat Haden, a former quarterback at the University of Southern California. One Monday night, on national television, after he had retired as a professional player, Haden stated, "You know, it's time for me to put a boy's game behind me and get on with the realistic work of the world." Should win-lose scenarios really only be a phase of growing up? We find, however, win-lose scenarios so prominent in all of our thinking.

Our incredible preoccupation with our adversary legal system is based on the fact that we believe such can always serve best in the delivery of justice. I suggest that in accord with the teachings of Augros and Stanciu, incidentally one a philosopher and one a physicist, in the book called *The New Biology,* we recognize that competition is useful, at times, perhaps in the evolutionary process of our early stages of our personal and organizational development, and that sooner or later, we will find that synergism, cooperation, and win-win scenarios may be the better way to effectively operate as a mature society and as mature people and to learn to deal with individuals on a far more constructive and just basis. One might also read *No Conflict* by psychologist A. Kron, who, along with Edward Deming, the architect of Japanese manufacturing and quality renaissance, claims that American industrial success has not been due to a "competitive" culture but to a large degree in spite of it; now that should shock pure free market proponents. We need, I believe, more win-win approaches to most of life's problems and challenges.

Myth Number Four

Competition in our corporate and economic world always serves the public well. Now, regarding this scenario I have some very strong views; I do not believe competition does always serve the public well. I believe competition serves the public well when we are dealing with human wants. It does not necessarily serve the public as well when we deal with human needs or human rights. I as an individual have absolutely no problem with the notion that society should learn how and when competition among our organizations and our people is effective, but we must also recognize where regulation, cooperation, and termination of investment in "overcompetitive" situations is appropriate. Anybody that thinks our phone system, our airline systems, and our health care programs are going to profit from unbridled competition among enterprises is, I think, suffering from severe delusion. The above myth, incidentally, is a subject in which I have great interest, and, along with Professor Nanus of the University of Southern California, am trying to work out some general guidelines to indicate where competition stops being useful and where cooperation should commence.

Myth Number Five

The basic purpose (and to some people the only purpose) of the industrial corporation is to make money for the stockholders. I do not believe this. The Japanese do not believe so and they are doing pretty well. In my opinion the basic purpose of the corporation is to take new and useful human knowledge, much of it generated by our academic institutions, move it into new products, processes, and services, with a value added consistent with and motivating the full process of wealth creation, and then move such into the marketplace for the benefit of a range of stakeholders—the customer, the society, the employees, the stockholders, and whoever else has a growing dependency on that corporate institution. Incidentally, I would like to suggest that historically, it is not impossible for "five star" academics to be interested in the particular wealth creating process. If any of you have the opportunity to visit Cambridge University, take a look at Isaac Newton's undergraduate diary in the Trinity College library. Newton was involved as an undergraduate in a loan business with his fellow students. When he was appointed chancellor of the Exchequeur or as they called it "Keeper of the Mint," he was delighted with the fact that he had found ways and means of possibly engineering a system that might eventually finance what later became the Industrial Revolution.

Myth Number Six

Our argumentative, conciliatory techniques in political processing and decision making are the best ways to strategize and enact future programming in social and economic domains. I believe that is nonsense. We have all seen the development over the last two hundred years of mathematical and experimental techniques that have promoted the dramatic evolution in science, medicine, engineering, etc. and that have revamped the oft-misguided medieval intuitive methods of making all kinds of decisions that do affect and have affected our lives. We now have techniques and procedures that allow us to be far more finite, that are more definite, and are more dependable than the methods by which we now make many decisions in our socioeconomic world. Most socioeconomic systems are counterintuitive in nature and really nonlinear feedback loop systems. Most such systems behave totally different than our common sense would predict, and much of which our political "do gooding" is intended to achieve actually makes matters worse. The liberal versus conservative scenario as a basis for political decision making, for example, is simply out of date and no longer relevant, if it ever was.

There's a new world of decision making useful in our social and economic domain and it's called "systems dynamics." Such has been initially developed and promoted by Professor Jay Forrester of the Massachusetts Institute of Technology. I think Forrester will be the Louis Pasteur of the socioeconomic culture and ills of the future. You should interest yourself in the background work and school of Dr. Forrester if you think you may be primarily interested in positively influencing social or socioeconomic environments. Incidentally, systems dynamics is being taught to high school students in Europe. It has not even been recognized in most of the college curriculums in the United States.

Myth Number Seven

The laws governing the physical and biophysical world around us, for example, the second law of thermodynamics, are separate and totally apart from any of those influences characterizing and affecting our social, human, and behavioral world. I don't believe this. I would suggest that once you enamored yourself of the potential ramifications of Heisenberg's uncertainty principle, and some of you may have already been exposed to such, and its impact for example on "free will" versus "determinism," you might pick up a couple of interesting little books. One of them is called *God and the New Biology* by Arthur Peacocke, who is a Cambridge professor of physical biochemistry and also an Anglican priest; the other is titled *God and the New Physics* by Paul Davies of the Newcastle University, England. I'm not too sure why the Anglican Church and the English academic world have pioneered this synergism of metaphysics, physics, and modern biology, but they certainly have.

Myth Number Eight

Progress and physical science have always been ahead of our understanding of so-called human behavioral sciences. I don't believe this is true. I think there has been dramatic learning and progress over the years in our so-called behavioral and human sciences well beyond our willingness to be guided thereby. We just *don't like* that which is predicated, proven, and rigorously indicated by human experience. I would suggest that if we ignored the laws of Newton the way we ignore the teaching of Thomas a'Kempis, Victor Frankl and perhaps from even more archaic times, Plato, Aristotle, and Lucretius, we'd all have broken legs as we daily jump out of buildings. Psychiatrist Dr. Will Menninger once said to me, when he was alive and head of the Menninger Foundation, "You know, Don, most of us, most of the time, know what we should do for the benefit of ourselves and those around us. We simply haven't the will to do it." I believe that human and behavioral science has historically taught us to a large extent what we should do for our own personal and social well-being. We just lack the self-discipline to accept same. I recommend strongly that we recognize that, as Mortimer Adler has stated, an education without a value system to guide human conduct and motivation probably necessarily enacted at a very young age is not education at all.

In Closing, Myth Number Nine

The education of our children and ourselves should always be pleasant, fascinating, and fun. It need not be frustrating, tiring, and incredibly hard work. I would like to read one comment by Mortimer Adler, the architect of the classic education world of the University of Chicago in the 1930s. His definition of the problem with education in our world today is as follows: "Education and interior transformation of a person's mind and character, a transformation that can be affected only through its own activity is as painful and is as exhilarating as any effort human beings make to make themselves better physically, emotionally or mentally. The practice of educators, even those well-intentioned who try to make learning less painful than it is, not only make it less exhilarating, but also weakens the mind and will on those to whom this fraud is perpetuated."

Again from Adler: "What every school boy doesn't know is that he doesn't know very much. However, precisely which every intelligent adult does know—is that he did not get an education in school. . . . The marks of a liberally educated person are not wealth or recognition, success in business or marriage, emotional stability, social poise or adaptation to his environment, good manners or even a good moral character. Each of these things is worth having, not in itself or for itself, but for the contribution to the fullness of a happy life. But none of this is the result of liberal education, though we may hope that liberal education does not oppose the acquisition and possession of some, if not all, of them.

"The direct product of liberal education is a good mind, well disciplined in its processes of inquiring and judging, knowing and understanding, well furnished with knowledge and well cultivated with ideas.

"When we realize that liberal learning must be carried on throughout each individual life as one of the main pursuits of leisure*, we can begin to estimate the full magnitude of the educational problem with which our society must cope for the first time in the history of mankind."

Graduating class, I challenge you to do one thing. Recognize that perpetual learning is probably the one thing that will produce that adventure in the human mind that is the basis of a true joy in living. Sometime you may realize that such is so rewarding and so satisfying that it has no substitute in any other thrill or mecca.

Thank you.

* I personally might say "life" rather than leisure.

EIGHT

A Future Renaissance in the Law

I N 1976 the American Assembly of Columbia University published a book entitled *Law and the American Future* (Prentice Hall). In this unique manuscript, a number of well-known personalities presented their individual comments, and Murray Schwartz, former dean of the University of California Law School, edited and abstracted their thoughts in a summary introduction.

Perhaps it might be of value to present a number of the views presented by the contributors in this analysis of future projections of American legal trends, and I would then also like to offer a few comments regarding Professor Schwartz's summary.

Philip Hauser, professor of urban sociology at the University of Chicago, in his presentation "Demographic Changes and the Legal System" noted that we are very different demographically from that society that created our basic legal structure. In population, birthrate, urban concentration, racial distribution, etc., we hardly resemble the population that ratified the Constitution of the United States and the Bill of Rights. Hauser further comments that the "social morphological revolution has produced a twentieth century demographic and technological world in which man is still trying to learn how to live. . . . Unprecedented problems have been cascaded and are likely to grow much worse before they grow any better." This, according to

Speech given to the Board of Overseers, Franklin Pierce Law Center, Concord, N.H., July 1987.

Hauser, is because we are attempting to deal with twentieth century problems with nineteenth, eighteenth, and prior century ideologies, values, and institutions, including law and government.

Included in our list of inherited beliefs, which seem incompatible with the reality of the interdependent and technological world we have created, are the following:

- That government is best which governs least.
- Each man in pursuing his own interest as if guided by an invisible hand acts in the interest of the collectivity.
- Cavaet emptor—let the buyer beware. Taxes are something the government takes away from the people and should be kept to a minimum.
- Labor has an inalienable right to strike and industry to lock out or shut down.
- National sovereignty must be preserved.
- Law and order must be maintained.

This list of shibboleths or social atavisms could be extended greatly. Considered in the context in which they are uttered at the present time, they are part of the American heritage that is anachronistic. They represent values which to a considerable extent are incorporated into law and which stand as obstacles to the resolution of the problems which confront us. They are evidences of "cultural lag"—the persistence of ideologies of the past in dissonance with the changed character of contemporary mass society.

Hauser continues: The function of law as stated by Edward Levi is "to develop concepts and to maintain and operate procedures that enable a sovereign community to be governed by rule for the common good, the attainment of human values, and to make that rule effective." But the law as it has evolved over time has not kept up either procedurally or substantively with the rapid changing social, economic, and political scene. The law as it has evolved is based in large part upon precedent, in part upon legislative enactment, and in part on judicial interpretation. All three of these sources of law are oriented more to the past than to the present or the future.

The problems which afflict American society cannot be resolved without fundamental changes in law and provisions for their implementation. There is need to reexamine and revise the law, and revise the law in the light of twentieth century demographic and technological reality.

In approaching revision of the law to conform with contemporary realities, it is desirable to recognize that neither a "conservative" nor a "liberal" approach is relevant. The "conservative" has been correctly defined as a person who worships dead radicals, and the "liberal" as the chap whose feet are firmly implanted in midair. The intuitive reactions of neither the conservative nor the liberal will adequately provide solutions for contemporary problems. What is required is a twentieth century approach—an engineering approach; that is, the resolution of problems through the application of knowledge, not a conservative or liberal approach.

Hauser further states that "it required about the century from 1750 to 1850 for the physical sciences to achieve enough respectability and acceptance so that the world turned to knowledge produced by the physical scientists for resolution of physical problems. The application of such knowledge is, of course, known as engineering. It is hardly necessary to observe that many centuries of bitter conflict with the 'establishment' were necessary before the findings of the physical sciences achieved respectability, acceptance, and application. It required about the century from 1850 to 1950 for the biomedical sciences to achieve enough respectability and acceptance so that the world turned to biological engineers for the resolution of the problems of health and life. Biological engineers are, of course, known as physicians and surgeons. *If this nation or the world is to survive, it may require the century from 1950 to 2050 for the social sciences to achieve enough respectability and acceptance so that social problems are resolved through the application of social science knowledge—through social engineering.*"

Kenneth Boulding, then professor of economics at the University of Colorado, insists that "there are unyielding limits on growth which apply to social systems as well as to individuals." Boulding's insistence that there are limits to the essential elements of growth (knowledge, energy, materials) is based on the concept that these have their own constraints, determined by principles of physics, such as entropy, as well as economics. "That material and energy may have some finite boundaries, as Schwartz also states, comes as no surprise; that the acquisition of knowledge may have similar limits is jolting news." I must state that I personally have trouble with the "limitation of knowledge" and I certainly believe that we have farther to go to reach a knowledge limit that limits characterizing energy and materials. Boulding asks, "What will be the impact on our legal system when we approach the limits of expansion?" To what extent are our most basic legal systems predicated on assumptions of infinite expansion, of upward mobility, of an ever expanding pie?

Douglas Cater, professor of communications and political science at Stanford University, states that "technological advances are epitomized by communication which introduces us to a world usually reserved for science fiction." Communication technology seems to be not merely driving but transforming mankind. "No one can deny that as a consequence of instant continuous pervasive and global communication, our relationships with each other and with the world around us are of a different order from those of past generations." The impact of the mass media on our social and political processes must give pause to both the staunchest defenders of First Amendment freedoms and those who regard the press and media less enthusiastically.

Social changes presenting equally profound problems are also in store for us. Concerned primarily with the work ethic and the family, Suzanne Keller, professor of sociology at Princeton, pictures a society in which our whole value of work may have to be altered. "How many of our basic legal doctrines are on the value—the morality—of labor, and the corruption of idleness?" Professor Keller asserts that we need new values; there is a lag between the norms we have inherited and on which many of our judicial decisions are based, and the realities we confront! "To what extent can, and should, our legal institutions accelerate the transformation of the ideal to the reality, or the reality to the ideal?"

Professor Kenneth Karst, then professor of law at the University of California, comments on the assessment of the individualism which has dominated our history—"competitive accumulation and consumption. . . . This individualism has its positive side; it releases energy; it provided for upward social and economic mobility; it promoted innovation and efficiency; it has offered a satisfactory living to the average person. . . . The negative side is that the system often assumes an insatiability of wants." Perhaps, in Browning's words, a man's reach should exceed his grasp; but asks Karst, "if the goal is obtained, must another always be sought?" Indeed Karst expresses his concern that the "achievement of communitarian social relationships and individual fulfillment—if those become our national goals—will tax our institutions for there will be increased tension in a future world between the demands of community on one hand, and individuality and privacy on the other."

I believe all of the above comments and questions proposed by the notable legal thinkers, economists, and sociologists certainly emphasize the concern earlier attributed to Professor Hauser that we are attempting to deal with twentieth century problems and situations (and I suggest opportunities) with nineteenth, eighteenth, and prior century ideologies, values, and institutions, including law and government. (I might add we should also question the cascading of court decisions, based on the accepted practice of assumed, related, and accepted practice of precedent—sometimes cascading "rationally" from an initial value or law that now obviously has no current relevance.) Unfortunately, as Thomas Hughes wrote a few years ago, at least half seriously, "One can say that the last quarter of the 20th century is currently made up of 14th century farmers, 15th century theologians, 16th century politicians, 17th century economists, 18th century bureaucrats, 19th century generals, and 21st century scientists. Walter Wriston has since added, "It's not a bad analysis, save for the American farmer, who certainly belongs to the 20th century." I might also add: We pay little attention to the Peter Drucker designation of ours as the "Age of Discontinuity"; we basically refuse to realize that much of the cause-effect relationships and validity of precedent that appeared valid only a short time ago are probably irrelevant in contemporary society.

I stated, earlier in my comments, that in addition to summarizing a few of the comments of the contributions to *Law and the American Future*" I would also comment on the summary comments by Professor Schwartz, its editor. Perhaps Schwartz's most dramatic and prevalent idea is his frequent concern for, and dependence on, Newton's third law of motion: "To every action there must be an opposed and equal reaction."

Professor Schwartz sees the solution of health problems and the subsequent overpopulation problem inescapably related; likewise the relation between the attractiveness of the cities and their uninhabitable state: The higher standard of living produced by industrialization and the fact that living has become progressively harder to endure is cause-effect-related in Schwartz's thought.

Schwartz also implies that Newton's third law is evident in man's response to new communication technology. "The great flow of information to the citizen-consumer has produced constant stimuli he shares with everyone else in society and to which he must respond instantly." It is certainly apparent in Professor Schwartz's comments, and it warms the heart of a scientist like myself, that anyone in the nontechnical society suggests that there are fundamentals of physical science principles that must be recognized as influencing behavioral, sociological, and legal phenomena. I would suggest, however, that Professor Schwartz's comments represent only a very introductory aspect of the probable influence of physical science laws and philosophy, as related to future social, legal, or economic culture.

Dr. Nicholas Herbert in his recent book *Quantum Reality* states that *"For better or worse, humans have tended to pattern their human, social, and political arrangement according to the then present dominant vision of physical reality.* Inevitably the cosmic view in vogue at the time trickles down to the most mundane details of everyday life. In the Middle Ages, when virtually everyone believed the world to be the personal creation of a divine being, society mirrored the hierarchy that supposedly existed in the heavens. Dante pictured this world as a series of concentric spheres, heaven the largest; next the planets' crystalline sphere; down through earth's concentric elements, the whole supported by the seven circles of hell."

This picture "gave everything and everyone his proper place in the medieval scheme of things, from the divine right of kings down to the abject obedience of the lowest serf. Most people accepted this hierarchical structure without question because it represented the way the world really is.

"The Newtonian revolution toppled the reign of crystal spheres and replaced it with the physics of ordinary matter governed by mathematical laws rather than divine command. The principal features of this Newtonian physics namely atomicity, objectivity, and determinism, were coincident with the rise and development of modern democracy which stresses a rule of the law rather than men, and which posits a theoretical equality between the parts of the social machinery." Dr. Herbert further states that the Declaration of Independence, for example,—"We hold these truths to be self evident" reads more like a mathematical theorem than a political document. The egalitarian mechanism that Newton discovered in the heavens has insinuated itself into every aspect of ordinary life. For better or worse, we live today in an assumed largely mechanistic world—the Newtonian "cause and effect" world that Professor Schwartz would have us take so seriously as we reconstruct and reconsider our social, legal, and economic structures. This mechanistic view of nature is closely related to rigorous determinism. The cosmic machine is seen as being completely causal and determinate. All that happened has a definite cause and gives rise to a definite effect and the future of any part of the system could, in principle, be predicted with certainty if its state at the time was known in all details. This Newtonian/Cartesian world had a most profound effect on all human institutions during the eighteenth and nineteenth centuries. There is in this system little room for Drucker's Age of Discontinuity.

Even, however, if we accept the Newtonian view of the world (the simple application of cause-effect logic to social, legal, and economic institutions), the subsequent formulation of a course of legal decision or economic programming to promote the public interest, the individual's well-being, or anything else is stacked with the need for entirely different techniques in "cause-effect" analysis and decision. As Forrester has stated in his *Urban Dynamics* human institutions are counterintuitive. The best of human minds can handle at most four or five variables in a cause-effect decision optimization process, and so many of the things that we do intuitively hoping to solve human problems and achieve desirable objectives actually make conditions worse. If we insist, however, in proceeding with deterministic concepts, we may find system modeling and computer evaluation more productive in ascertaining the significant leverage points in our system than relying on "obvious common sense" and erroneous intuitive cause-effect relationships.

Unfortunately, however, just as Newton shattered the medieval crystal spheres, modern quantum theory has irreparably smashed the Newton clockwork. We are now certain that the world is not a deterministic mechanism. "The current search for physical reality through quantum mechanics is a search for a single image that does justice to our new knowledge of how the world actually works."

Many aspects of quantum theory are public knowledge—at least to the curious—to the learners as contrasted to the knowers of our world. One concept, the Heisenberg uncertainty principle, which actively forbids the accuracy of certain knowledge, conflicts dramatically with our desire for, and comfort in, certainty. The new view of our physical world is perfectly happy with the world of probabilities and behavioral distribution—it deals little with certainty for individual entities.

Fritjof Capra, in his provocative book *The Turning Point*, states that the revolution in modern physics foreshadows an imminent revolution in all sciences and a transformation in our worldview and values. The major problems of our times are all different facets of one and the same crisis, which is essentially a crisis of perception. The crisis derives from the fact that we are trying to apply the concepts of an outdated worldview—Cartesian-Newtonian science—to a a reality which can no longer be understood in terms of such concepts. The application of *Cartesian-Newtonian* thinking, with its cause-effect preoccupation, has brought us to a perilous impasse in all aspects of our human institutions.

I agree with Professor Schwartz and Professor Hauser that there are implications in physical science and engineering disciplines that must be considered in our advancement of human institutions, including "The Law." I would suggest, however, that we not be over-preoccupied with Schwartz's concern for Newton's third law or Hauser's orientation toward pragmatic engineering systems.

I should like to add another concept for consideration as we *deliberate* any future Renaissance in the Law. In addition to concerning ourselves with a compatibility between proposed legal values and the status of our understanding of physical reality, I suggest that we give consideration to experimental demonstration and experimental validation of the effectiveness and rationality of a law, regulation, or decision before we accept the conclusion that our action represents a viable path to establish or protect a desired condition. We certainly don't want a decision to be an expression of a value incompatible with new realities, or perhaps intractably associated with old now irrelevant values or outmoded effectiveness.

We must also recognize that existing laws or regulations may be simply the result of "a march" of a trend, undetectable at first, wherein a series of incremental precedents have produced a condition inconsistent with the most rational and adventurous or original intent.

One of the most apparent, and I think indefensible, cultures and attitudes currently existing within legal decision and social attitude is that if something negative happens to a person, or some desirable effect fails to occur (all perceived from the viewpoint of the subject), then someone else is *at fault*. Indeed the scenario has advanced to the point where even in the absence of an apparent culprit, someone should or must pay. This set of attitudes, often supported and advanced by our courts, is certainly possibly viable only under the Newtonian view of the universe. A modern view of the physical world would give no credibility to this view.

Another apparent preoccupation, totally inconsistent with economic or business reality, is that competition between individuals or corporations is inherently good and almost always serves the well-being of overall society. There is no experimental or historical validity to this assumption and much of the conduct of the courts is totally out of phase with current and much historical evidence. It is relatively easy, for example, to show that competition is useful only in a relatively distinct part of a product life cycle, when demand exceeds supply, when the initial stage of innovation and entrepreneurship have matured, and before the life cycle of the product has turned down as a function of market growth and/or profitability. Increased competition in mature phase of a product life cycle only tends to prematurely eliminate many useful products from the marketplace. Our patent laws, which have done more than most courts understand to establish the historical predominance of American industry in world markets, were a specific attempt to eliminate competition in the initial phase of a new unique product life; these laws served us well.

Perhaps one of the most destructive cultures and habits existing within our legal and total social structure is the prevalence of the win-lose conduct so accepted in our society as bringing out the best in individuals and institutions and effective in establishing the most viable solutions to human and legal confrontation. Few authors have questioned this attitude more effectively than Paul A. Weiss, one of the world's most distinguished experimental and theoretical biologists (Rockefeller University).

Weiss states—"Any patterned living system be it a cell, an organism, a community, or a society—is held together as a viable integrated entity by inner ties that are elastic; the system yields to moderate distortion, and the greater the distortion, the greater is also the counterforce that contains it within bounds. This strain, however, can be sustained only up to a certain limit. If stretched beyond, the bonds will snap: the system loses its cohesion, crumbles, flies apart. Just think of whirling an object on a rubber string round and round at increasing speed until centrifugal force breaks the string and the object flies off. This is the way in which antagonisms give rise to schisms: by promoting centrifugal disruption. Our world is full of examples. Issues are artificially polarized, the spotlight being turned on the extremes, and then the tug-of-war between them goes on and on. The playful spirit of win-or-lose of the sports field, with friendly handshakes at the end, is now too often violently perverted into a do-or-die precept for either-or survival. Antagonisms that have started from sheer accentuation of extreme points of view deteriorate into factual conflict and combat, and people change from occupants of opposite ideological stations into actual aggressive opponents.

"This tendency for extremes to rise through emphasis and prominence to eventual total separation is deeply ingrained in the nature of biological existence. Biological nature condones the resolution of conflict by victory rather than by conciliation. Being the animal he is, man has inherited a flair for polarizing issues. Instinctively, he even fans their conflict-breeding potential by laying stress on divergence and disparity; doing so, he amplifies the separative forces which threaten to disrupt the crucial cohesiveness without which no living system, including the human race, can survive. In short, biological man cannot be trusted to act in the best interest of humanity.

"But then, man is much more than an animal. Through his power of reasoning, he can, if not abolish his deep-set instincts, at least repress and supersede them by intelligent action. Rational foresight lets him spot danger signals of strain approaching stress limit, and insight, gained from experience, enables him to take counter measures in time to forestall imminent disaster by brake-like damping, decelerating and draining the motive force of extreme swings in attitude. In principle, such deliberate regulatory intervention by man corresponds, of course, to the automatic 'negative feedback' devices to which any self-preserving system, living or nonliving, owes its capacity for maintaining, or oscillating about, a state of relative stability of pattern. Yet, human corrective counteractions differ from those of technological created automatons in their lack of built-in self restraints: a human counterthrust started as a control act often ends up losing its own self-control.

"We have all seen prominent individuals' violent aversion to an excessive swing in one direction, reverse the wave into one no less extreme, even though of opposite sign.

"Yes, biological man tends to create antagonisms by emphasizing the extreme ends of a continuous spectrum of notions composed of truths, as well as fallacies and prejudices; that civilized man, although he has the rational endowment to counteract that fatal trend to excessive polarization, seems not to have as yet learned to make the most of his rational faculties by adopting the broad perspective which would let moderation defuse the explosive charge of fanatical antagonisms.

"This is a state of affairs in which education (and I add 'The Law') should assume a major corrective and preventive function, ending it may be the primary function of education. The task would be to break the obsessive habit of focusing compulsively on single isolated issues, and develop in its stead the habit of letting the mind sweep back and forth over the whole continuum of phenomena, which constitute the real context. This evidently would imply a major change of attitude, a reorientation of viewpoint and focus of thoughts from centrifugal decomposition to something that has ability to unify convergence. Physical science, with its rigorous methodology, combined with logic, might perhaps be more incisive and convincing in illustrating the middle-of-the-road way to harmony than have been the compromises of legal conciliation. or political accommodation. Science has had a good record of success in resolving tenacious sham controversies by proving opposing tenets to be not mutually exclusive, but rather validly coexisting alternatives.

"Our theme should be the recognition and scientific validation of the rule of order that pervades the universe and culminates in human understanding.

"Civilized man must recognize ideological extremes for what they are: artificially disconnected opposite ends of continuous scales of intergrading values, just fortified in their positions of antagonistic isolation by verbal symbolism and the instinctual vestiges in man of his biological past."

Obviously, if we are to heed Professor Weiss's concerns in our renaissance of the law and its basic attitudes, we must perhaps question the fundamental character of our adversarily and litigation-oriented legal system.

In a less biological but more psychologically oriented approach to the same issue (the competitive win-lose culture), Theodore Rubin, the eminent New York psychiatrist, states: "Competition is a residual of the primitive past, and is not a genetic residual. It passes on to us through training in our society from generation to generation; it is addictive; it contributes to paranoia." Cooperation, not competition brings out the best in us and has been the basis for all dependable real human progress. Man has evolved to the point of his progress that he now enjoys in spite of the competitive and adversarial attitudes that fascinate American society. Modern civilization has survived not because of adversarial relationships which have their basis in man's early biological evolution, but because of symbiotic relationships that take place within the evolution of the species.

Is a legal system that obviously assumes competitive, adversarily oriented, win-lose resolution capable of change to a win-win cooperation preoccupation and hence become more compatible with basic biological psychological perception of modern mature mentality?

One final cultural attitude, with its attending legal and judicial support so apparent in our society, is the widespread attitude that morality, right, and good are now somehow predominantly supportive of the underdog or "low man on the totem pole." This attitude permeates economic position, social position, national origin, racial character, etc. America, and too often its legal structure, has become a champion and supporter and lover of the underdog, regardless of whether the underdog's position is based on any rational justified support or entitlement. Indeed our correlation between right and good position in society has totally flip-flopped and reversed in the past one hundred years. The correlation of 1885 was just as irrelevant as that now existing in 1985 and any attempt to parallel "right" and economics, social status, etc. serves neither the individual nor society.

Summarizing, a future Renaissance in "The Law" must, it would appear:

1. Suggest harmony and concurrence with the prevalent and dominant view of physical reality existing at any time. Such would certainly demand that the basis of the law must be dynamic and not constrained by outmoded ideologies and values, regardless of how well those ideologies and values have historically served. We must also recognize that the current Age of Discontinuity can invalidate much of the utility of precedent-established decisions.
2. Suggest consistency with the fundamental realities of the systematic organized body of applicable interrelated concepts that are valid enough to stand up under the test of experimental demonstration and experimental validation, and represent a common consistent experience at least within that society where such experiences are observed and that "The Law" is destined to serve.
3. Be consistent with and promote the increasingly evident basic nature of mature man, a creature whose greatest potential lies in cooperation, not competition, in win-win situations, not win-lose scenarios.

We have, in our society in the last three decades, witnessed a growth of laws and regulations that permeate every phase of human life and conduct. Alexander Solzhenitsyn commented several years ago: "[I] have led most of my life in a society that is devoid of the virtues of any aspect of rational law and to live such a life in such an environment is an intolerable experience indeed. To live life, however, in an environment that is primarily governed by rules, regulations, and law is a miserable experience also, because it is inconsistent with and noncontributing to the spirit of the people whom it designs to serve."

I believe that any well-meaning and constructively intended organization or institution or society that is overwhelmed by laws and regulations probably finds itself in the situation because the clarity, effectiveness, and poignancy of the motivating concepts on which the organization bases its existence have either become lost in antiquity and memory, or have become anachronistic because the world has changed but the institution's supporting concepts have not. Such would suggest that any institution—"The Law" is no exception—will retain its effectiveness, digestibility, and motivating capability only when it clearly and continuously demonstrates its compatibility with changing reality and persuades society of the validity of the concepts on which the values of that institution are based. This would suggest that the institution must assume a responsibility for continuous presentation of its basic concepts and values to any social unit it hopes to influence. "The Law" like any institution must assume the role of an educational force, and a creator of new dynamic realistic concepts on which it is based—and have a research and cognitive capability to establish those concepts.

I believe we must create within our American legal educational establishment a new type of law school—an institution based not so much on teaching consistence with precedent as with awareness of discontinuity, not so much with teaching established obvious legal religion but with research into the effects of new concepts of our universe, into the effects of new knowledge in biology, psychology, behavioral science, economics, etc., and the synergism of that new knowledge into a force influencing the totality of legal premises and practice—a school that is primarily motivated and known by its graduate scholars, research, and graduate education, and whose undergraduates are exposed to the renaissance concepts resulting from such research. The new school must also assume a role of educating the public regarding the basic philosophies and concepts on which our current legal perceptions are based. We need in the world of legal education an institution parallel to Cal Tech in the physical sciences, small and poignant, unequalled in its vanguard activity, and attracting the best in curiosity and conceptualizing talent.

NINE

The Role of Top Management in the Innovation and Entrepreneurial Process

Mr. Alstadt argues that corporations today need leaders with "a feel" for science, technology, the entrepreneurial process, and innovation.

"Executives spend a relatively small percentage of their day in the development of new product and market strategy or playing any significant role in seeing that the innovation process is effectively implemented. Do we need to look further to find some of the reasons for the basic demise of some of our American corporations?"
—DONALD M. ALSTADT

The subject that I have chosen is "The Role of Top Management in the Innovation and Entrepreneurial Process." I say that the chief executive's role ought to be a lot more dynamic and a lot more involved than it is in most companies in the United States.

Later I will deal with the basic purpose of the corporation, for I think that if we clarify what a corporation really does in our society, it may stimulate some of our corporate officers and corporate heads to think differently about the innovation process. Such may also stimu-

Speech given at the National Conference for Deans, Business and Engineering Schools, December 1980, St. Louis, Mo.

late a selection of corporate officers toward a somewhat different breed than has been the case in the past.

We know that it is difficult for some parts of our society to recognize today that a very necessary aspect of our corporate life is the making of a profit—and also that a very necessary aspect of government operation is fiscal responsibility. I don't think anybody here, however, is going to deny these statements. It is even more difficult, however, for many executives to understand, in both our domestic economy and in our national and international situation, that innovation and not solely the making and managing of money may be the primary and most immediate challenge before our corporate and government institutions. America today, I believe, will retain its industrial, economic, and military preeminence only by an appreciation throughout society of the importance of technological innovation, and the entrepreneurial application of discovery, that has come about through the R and D process. This process, regardless of how it is done, is the primary factor by which America and the West have achieved and maintained their dominant world position both economically and militarily. That much of our corporate and government leadership does not understand and has never been directly involved in the process of technological innovation may be the Achilles heel that will jeopardize the future economic growth of this country and indeed its national survival.

I know that it is hard for many people to face the fact that science and technology and not government manipulation, fiscal or economic action, are probably the most powerful forces for positive change in the world today. That any particular change may be valued as good or bad, moral or otherwise, does not alter this basic fact.

Unfortunately, much of the world leadership, in both corporate and governmental institutions, does not recognize the past 150 years as a period in which the human race for the first time in history could hope that tomorrow might be better than today. Such hope is largely a result of the wealth-creating capabilities of the industrial revolution. Science and technology have become the primary architects of positive change, human condition, and history. We are still writing history books as though worn-out philosophies and their associated dichotomies are the prime movers in society. When men began to walk into the laboratories in greater and greater numbers, mankind really began a rapid climb out of a world of hopelessness and discouragement. It was then that the idea that "tomorrow might be better than today," a concept which had never existed before, began to be a reality. I never realized this fact until I read the book by Heilbroner entitled *The Future as History*.

You know, most of the world's technological capability is not being effectively utilized to alleviate the world's economic problems and suffering. And I think, unfortunately, that the people in government who are responsible for the ultimate decisions and policies in our society are for the most part not aware of this "information lag." But such is not the main subject of my thoughts. I am more concerned about the fact that I hear of so many instances in which heads of basic research or heads of R and D functions in our companies complain that they have achieved breakthroughs in the laboratory, in product or process possibilities that could possibly rejuvenate the industry or the company, but that the lack of understanding and lack of feel on the part of the top management or the chief executive officer regarding these breakthroughs, and the lack of entrepreneurial interest or ability on the part of the whole organization, prevent further utilization. I would like to give you an example of the situation. About ten years ago I was talking with the director of research of one of the major steel companies of the United States. This particular vice president for research said, "In my laboratory we have breakthroughs that could remake both the process and product profile of this corporation. My marketing manager's idea of a breakthrough in the laboratory is a new process for the factory which, if introduced, can help undersell his competition on what he is now selling, undersell them by 20 or 25 percent. He does not really want a new product. The production manager's idea of a new breakthrough is a new product that he can make using his current equipment. He does not really give a damn what it is as long as he does not have to change the plant." He continued, "You know, I do not object to those two attitudes on the part of these people. But then we all walk into the president's office and the president looks at the three of us and says, 'When you guys can agree, come back in.'" He said, "This attitude is a very disappointing and unfortunate situation characterizing our company."

Much has been written about the current relative position of American research productivity and American technological strength. Some authors have contended that our research posture has never been better. Others say that the lack of research investment over the last four, five, ten years spells future military and economic disaster for both our country and our corporations. I do not intend to engage here in a discussion of the quality of our research, or of the current magnitude. I am far more concerned with the environment in which this innovation process must take place, that is, the total innovation process, that is, the movement of an idea through the process of R and D invention, through the product reality, through the entrepreneurial stage in the market, and into an ongoing reality as a business.

England, over the years, for example, has displayed the highest quality of research capability and even development: jet engines, antibiotics, polymeric materials. But the government, corporate, and social structure of Britain certainly has not been conducive to optimizing these innovations for the real benefit of the country.

Since 1945 we have witnessed some rather dramatic changes in the attitudes of the American government and the American corporation and the American public toward popularity. Government and industry appropriated huge amounts of money for basic research. Large segments of the government administration and corporate management then sat back and waited for research to display its magic power. These passive observers were frequently disappointed, and particularly in our corporations.

We then witnessed in the late '50s another significant development. Research and development must, many managements claimed, be channeled by the state and the evident wants and needs of the marketplace. The marketing executives gained unprecedented power over the selection of R and D projects. History indicates that real new product innovation was rarely the result. Product modification or improvement was the normal achievement. The words of Cyril Smith, Institute Professor here at MIT, must be heeded. "History shows that technology originated far more often in curiosity and aesthetic urges than in perceived usefulness. Necessity is not the mother of invention—only of improvement."

The economic recession of the early 1960s witnessed the placement in general management of individuals whose background and training were primarily finance. Expenses had to be cut. All too frequently the relatively far-out research was the first casualty. What made the situation ridiculous is that basic research is relatively cheap considering what the high payout will be when successful research is really supported and then programmed by competent corporate executive leadership. Why did all this happen? Why have all of these so-called fads, if you will, imposed themselves on our corporations since 1955? Quite accidentally in 1951 I had the pleasure of sitting next to Irving Langmuir when he was the dean of American scientists. He said something which I have never forgotten. He said: "The most formidable threat to research and innovation in this country is the growing number of executives and politicians who are making decisions affecting research policy and expenditure, whose training and experience does not permit them to understand what it is all about." Need we say more?

Carl Prutton, former dean of Case and later chief research executive officer of one of America's largest corporations, said, "To realize ultimate potential from research requires comprehension and active participation by top corporate management. General and executive management has a greater responsibility for the overall end result, successful economic prosecution, and success in the marketplace, than does a research manager of the research organization. In a modern era of rapidly changing technology when corporate general management is selected, the ability to effectively program research and technology is becoming an absolute requirement." The individuals who guided the growth of companies like DuPont, Texas Instruments, Hewlett-Packard, IBM, Polaroid, and 3M understood this principle very clearly. Such institutions have been growing at three times the rate of their low-technology counterparts, producing new employment almost ten times as rapidly, improving productivity at twice the rate, and increasing prices only 20 percent as far as low-technology counterparts.

I am always fascinated by the fact that when I come to a meeting such as this involving the subject of R and D, innovation, new product development, or entrepreneurship, things that involve changing the organization's technology or product profile, I find few chief executive officers. Now the presidents will allow and maybe encourage their associates from the R and D functions to go, but they rarely if ever show up themselves.

Let us now consider the primary mission of our corporations. I know what many people would say: It is to make money for the stockholders. Well, if this is the primary mission, if this is the reason for the corporation's existence, I would suggest that many corporations ought to be liquidated, sold at book value, and the money invested in tax-exempt bonds. Most corporations most of the time do not make 6 percent ROA after taxes. Making profit is a very necessary tactic in the operation of our corporations. The more we make, legitimately, the better. I think there is a more basic reason for the existence of the American corporations. And I would like to go to the blackboard and put on it a little diagram.

$$\text{MISSION} = \int_{L_1}^{L_2} \int_{O_1}^{O_2} \int_{F_1}^{F_2}$$

$$T \rightarrow P \rightarrow M$$

The corporation is here and was started primarily by its founders to take useful human knowledge (which is technology), move same into products or services, and move such into the marketplace.

Such is what motivates people to start corporations. Founders fully know that if they are successful, they will make money. They know that if they are to stay alive, they have to make money. But they pursue a profit to enable the organization to carry out this T-P-M process represented by my simple triple integral. They do this within whatever financial limits the corporation must accept ($F_1 F_2$), within whatever organization and manpower limits the company might have ($O_1 O_2$), and within whatever the legal limits that they must recognize ($L_1 L_2$). I keep telling our vice presidents in charge of these limits, "Look, your job is to open up those limits. Do not narrow them." And I would like to say the same thing to the government. "You must help me open up the limits—like the Japanese government does." My primary preoccupation and function as chief executive officer is to enact the procedure under the integral sign. Industry should recognize that this is its basic function, and if top management accepts this as the basic reason for the corporation's existence, the corporation will likely survive. I think long-term survival is more of a challenge for our corporations than a short-term profit. Only if top management accepts this survival responsibility will a given corporation continue to serve all of its stakeholders. By stakeholders I mean the customers, the stockholders, the employees, and society in general. You know, we often say that the stockholders really run and own the company.

I have often wondered what would happen if all of the stockholders in the General Electric Company, as an example, met somewhere and decided, "Today we are going to liquidate the company." Do you really think this could happen? I think the next morning the unions, the government, etc., would make sure that General Electric somehow continues to serve its mission. We have made sure that Lockheed and Chrysler continue to serve their mission, even when these companies do not make a profit; other stakeholders had to be served. The various stakeholders' voices are becoming at least as loud as that of the stockholders and in many places louder. Consider what happened recently at Dow. During a talk I had recently with an officer of Dow, he said: "You know, we have far fewer rumblings from and troubles with our stockholders than we have with the public in general. We found this out at our gates one day when a crowd was demonstrating about napalm. We never expected anybody to harass such nice midwestern boys the way we got hell."

If science and technology are the most powerful agents for change, and if advancing them is the primary function of a corporation, then we must face the fact that we probably need "leaders" of a different type, possessing different types of training and experience, than those that have historically managed the majority of our corporations. I say the majority; I am not talking about organizations the likes of which are represented here today. But the fact that you are here means that you are an exception to the rule. IBM, 3M, DuPont, Hewlett-Packard, Texas Instruments are exceptions. The great bulk of the American corporations, however, are not in that wonderful spot where technological innovation is saving them in world market competition. I have used the word "leader" in contrast to the word "manager" when I say I think many of our corporations are overmanaged and underled. Leadership implies, in addition to the effective management of an institution, that added ability to conceptualize what the future could be. Without this conceptualizing ability at the top of an organization, the process of innovation through the use of new knowledge will be seriously inhibited, if it occurs at all.

I do not know how many of you saw a fascinating article in a recent issue of *Harvard Business Review* entitled "Managing Technology: A Box of Cigars for Brad." It clearly pointed out that the preoccupation of many top managements with current problems, legal matters, financial manipulation, personnel activity, now dominates a disproportionate amount of the executive's time. Executives spend a relatively small percentage of their day in the development of new product and market strategy or playing any significant role in seeing that the innovation process is effectively implemented. Do we need to look further to find some of the reasons for the basic demise of some of our American corporations?

I would suggest that a number of changes be enacted in corporations and society in general.

One: I think governments must encourage the leaders of corporations to accept innovation as a primary responsibility. Government cannot by its endless regulations and paperwork force corporate management to spend most of its time as a legalistic umpire and accounting scorekeeper, and to assume the role of operating second-class welfare agencies. Executives must become deeply involved in this ballgame called innovation.

Incidentally, I enjoy telling a little story about government regulation. I tell it perhaps as a bit of levity to interrupt the monotony of my speech. I think, however, the tale does emphasize a point. Back in 1885 a young man was brought to Pasteur by his parents. He had been bitten by a dog with rabies. I never realized until recently that there is only one case history in medicine wherein somebody with rabies has recovered without treatment. Joseph Meister had rabies, and his parents wanted Pasteur to inoculate the young man. Pasteur had little clinical evidence that his vaccine was safe or effective. But the boy was going to die anyway. So the parents prevailed on Pasteur to inoculate the child. Pasteur inoculated the child and Joseph Meister fortunately recovered promptly. Joseph Meister died only eight years ago at a ripe old age of ninety-five or thereabout. Each day of his life, Joseph, while passing Pasteur's tomb in Les Invalids, left a little flower. I often wondered where Meister would have been all those years if there had been an aggressive federal drug agency in France in 1885. Well, I suspect he would have long been dead. I mention his unusual incident to emphasize a point.

Two: Corporations and government, I believe, must place in the key management positions people who have a feel, not extended knowledge like the people in the R and D organization, but "a feel" for science, technology, the entrepreneurial process, and innovation. The continued increase of the legalistic mentality, particularly in America, at the top the corporate and government institutions is going to do little to enable us to promote the entire innovative process in industry. Promoting the legalistic mentality is the latest fad in reactive crisis-oriented managerial selection. We have recently changed from promoting the finance man to promoting the legal man into the top job. We put everybody at the top of our organizations except those whose primary responsibility and interest is enacting the process in my integral equation.

Three: I think the American industrial scene and the American technological corporation need, in the American universities, an entirely different kind of school of management (or preferably a school of leadership) than has been characteristic in the past of our graduate schools of business. I do not think the average business school in this country is adequate for the retraining and upgrading of management and leadership for technology-based companies. I think most of you know that if you are going to take people and retrain them for service in hotel management, you send them to Cornell or Denver. The reason is quite evident—they learn something about hotels while they are at Cornell or Denver.

I was surprised six months ago while visiting one of the more prestigious eastern business schools to hear the dean say, "For twenty-five years we have done nothing except train people to massage the existing institution. We have given people little indication or awareness of the need for injecting into that institution new technology, new products, new entrepreneurial spirit." He said, "We are going to change this." I was astounded because although I often hear this desire expressed by engineering school deans, I do not very often hear it from the lips of a business school dean. For years I have believed that business school deans and engineering school deans must be placed in the same room, and forced to talk about innovation. I would also have desired university presidents be placed in that room; they may synergize the willing and unwilling components of their institutions.

In closing, I would just like to state that I do not believe that these problems related to the need for increased innovation, participation between university groups and the university and the corporation, etc. are insoluble. Many of the difficulties would dissolve very rapidly if top management of our corporations would get into the innovation ball game. I also do not buy some of the myths that I have heard expressed here and elsewhere, that the small corporation cannot do R and D, and that the small corporation cannot do basic research. Incidentally, in the same breath these people will say that a large corporation is too inflexible to utilize the fruits of these once such is done. If we buy both these concepts we are really in the mud. I do not buy either one of them. There are large corporations with amazing flexibility and adaptability in enacting and utilizing innovation. And there are small corporations that do very effective basic research and get the results moved through their organizations. I think those two myths are something we ought not to take seriously.

Face the fact, however, that if our whole process of innovation is going to get into high gear, top management of our institutions must assume the process as one of their major responsibilities.

TEN

Overregulation Inhibits America's Innovative Spirit

Mr. Alstadt warns against overregulation, which can in-
hibit the dynamic, innovative spirit of the American public.
He illustrates his point by contrasting the approaches of
"principle-based" and "regulation-based" managements.

*"Widespread presence of regulation in any institution results in the
enervation of the organization, a transfer of movement from a proactive, opportunity-oriented mood to a reactive and risk-minimizing
one."*
    —DONALD M. ALSTADT

I would like to speak today not as a president of a corporation. I would
like to speak as a person who is involved with a wide variety of social
institutions, including institutions of higher learning and major health
centers. I have a strong interest in academic institutions as some of
you people in Pittsburgh know. If I were to speak solely from that
vantage point, of a person involved with a large number of educational
institutions and not the corporate world per se, I would say that if I
could suddenly "straighten out" one institution in this state, it would

Speech given at the Conference on Government Regulatory Practices,
1981, Pittsburgh, Penn.

be the Board of Education in the Commonwealth of Pennsylvania. When I was asked four years ago if I would accept a position on the State Board of Education, I sent back a letter describing my views, and I never received a reply. I guess my views were not very compatible with the views held at the time. Why start my comments with a reference to the Pennsylvania Board of Education? Simply because it represents a classic example of a specific sickness in the organizational maturation I see occurring in America—that of overregulation.

As you know, you have to tell a joke to get a speech under way, so I will tell one. As a matter of fact, it isn't really a joke; it is a strange true story. Back in about 1894 or 1895, a young man, ten years old, was brought to the Paris laboratory of Louis Pasteur. He was suffering from a rabies bite, which at that time meant two weeks of extreme suffering and then death. There was no known way to avoid death. Pasteur, of course, had been very effective in treating cattle for anthrax and in saving crops and various other things. He had a vaccine for rabies on the shelf and had never used it. He did not at first want to use it on anybody; he had no laboratory experience with it at all. The parents of little Joseph Meister begged Pasteur, to whom they had been sent by the medical profession, to inoculate the boy. Pasteur resisted very strongly, even in the absence of regulations from the EPA, or an FDA, or any other similar organization. Finally, the tears of the mother and father prevailed and Pasteur inoculated this boy. Incidentally, Pasteur did this without the support of his colleagues; they were not convinced that the vaccine, even though prepared by the "anthrax" technique, would be effective. Little Joseph Meister didn't die; he didn't get sick. The next two or three years saw people from all over Europe coming to get their rabies shots. That was the beginning of the elimination of that horrible disease of the nineteenth century. What many don't know is that Joseph Meister only died about five years ago. He was up in his nineties. Every day on his way to work, Joseph put a rose on the tomb of this great man. I have often wondered when I look at Pasteur's statue, "Where would Joseph be had Pasteur been subjected to the limitations on experimental innovation (or to the FDA) —even if he thought he was doing the 'right' thing—a situation that our patients and our medical profession often confront today?" One of the most distinguished medical researchers in this country, Dr. Yukihiko Nose, told me that if something doesn't change in this country in the next ten years, the medical research brains in this country will leave. They will be doing their work in England, Germany, Japan, and elsewhere. I would hate to see that happen.

Now with my expression of annoyance with the State Board of Education and the FDA, perhaps I can get through my speech.

A number of weeks ago, I received a letter from a distinguished senator from Pennsylvania in answer to a letter that I had sent. He said to me, "This is a nation based on laws." I told him that I would like to correct the assumption that this is a nation based on laws. This is a nation primarily based on concepts, and principles, and ideas, and visions. The laws came along when necessary, usually where unavoidable, to make certain that the majority or *even* a belligerent minority of people that were causing trouble for the rest did abide by principles, concepts, and ideas. If I were to today express my major concern—whether I am dealing with hospitals or industry, school systems, or a private academic university—it is that we do not enact a system of regulation, a system of rules, in this country so intense, so inhibiting that the natural and long-standing *effective,* dynamic innovative spirit of the American public is in any way injured, comes to a halt, or accepts the frustration now developing. We must promote ideas and concepts—not rules and regulations.

Those who teach in business schools understand that we can classify organizations in many ways. One way to classify them is to group them as either "principle based" or "regulation based." We all know the difference that is inherent. Organizations based on concepts and principles hopefully demonstrate an inherent leadership and a persuasiveness of a proactive organization, dedicated to the enactment of new horizons and new insights. There are some very specific characteristics of such an organization. Basically proactive, it is motivated by concepts and ideas that maximize opportunity. It does not attempt to minimize risk; it is not problem or crisis oriented primarily. It primarily emphasizes opportunity at a tolerable risk. It manages somehow to *solve* its problems with enthusiasm on the part of the people involved. It is change-oriented and not primarily dedicated to emulating actions of the past. The organization looks at conflicts in a win-win context rather than an adversary-oriented win-lose profile; the word authority isn't heard very often, the word responsibility is. It is exciting; it tends to be underadministered, undermanaged, and appropriately led. It attempts to *achieve*, sometimes in unexpected ways, because it brings out the best in people.

Now what about the opposite type of organization? Incidentally, our public school system has gone from my first "type" example to my second "type" example. The second type is reactive because it is primarily motivated by miscellaneous responses to a variety of pressures from the environment. It tends to minimize risk and opportunities at the same time. It is problem and crisis oriented. It usually seems to be in a confused flap. It resists change, except that which will return everything to the wonderful world of yesterday, even if old suffering returns. It does not help people to grow. It does not delegate; the word authority is always present; the word responsibility is seldom heard. In any conflict, it is a win-lose situation; rules must be served. It tends to be overmanaged, overadministered, and underled. It tends to underachieve, and does not develop people.

If I seem to be making a distinction between leadership of an institution and management of it, I certainly am. The real distinction between managing an organization and leading it is the ability on the part of the person who is at the top of the institution to be concerned about what the future could be. A widespread presence of regulation in any institution results in the enervation of the organization, a transfer of movement from a proactive, opportunity-oriented mood to a reactive and risk-minimizing one. Widespread regulation in any society or any organization reflects an absence of visionary leadership, an inadequate supply of ideas, and inadequate persuasive capacity. This is what is happening to our society—and to much of our public education system in particular.

The movement from proactive opportunity orientation to a reactive risk-minimizing position is the reason why we are "drifting" in certain of our institutions. I am not limiting my comments to government, for this drifting is happening in corporations, in academic circles, in hospitals—it does not require a federal government per se to start the institutional ball rolling toward a reactive status. However, in too many places in our government institutions, we are becoming a nation of mechanistic legality and control—a nation lacking in concepts and not guided by conceptual vision. Thomas Hughes once wrote, about a half decade ago, "The twentieth century is currently made up of fourteenth century farmers, fifteenth century theologians, sixteenth century politicians, seventeenth century economists, eighteenth century bureaucrats, nineteenth century generals, and twenty-first century scientists." "Not a bad analysis, except the American farmer belongs in the twentieth century," says Walter Wriston.

There is lack of awareness in many segments of our society, particularly in the sociopolitical area, regarding the information and knowledge that exists at the present time that can be immediately applied for the benefit of all mankind. This information lag, the complete unawareness on the part of much of our society of what is really known at the present time, compared to what is actually applied, is probably the most widespread cause for suffering of the multitudes of the world. Unfortunately, the people who run and operate most of our institutions and who are responsible for decisions affecting our people and many institutions are not, for the most part, aware of this. They are, for example, not aware of what is feasible (as a decision-making technique) that would allow us to solve many of our problems and many of the current social conflicts. I would predict, incidentally, that we are seeing a growth of this technique (systems dynamics) which will allow many of the segments of our society to use the more rigorous methods of physical scientists for the solution of social problems. Jay Forester says that our society is primarily based on institutions which are, for example, counterintuitive in nature; the intuitive do-gooding in the world is usually full of unexpected pitfalls and leads to extremely unfortunate circumstances. Nevertheless, in summarizing, this information gap between what is really known by some segments of our society and what is not known by others has set up the possibility of conflict and misunderstanding between people. This conflict and misunderstanding make resolution and utilization of knowledge very difficult.

A second condition which produces problems in our public and sociopolitical institutions is the absence of exceptional leadership in such institutions. We have a preponderance in many of our institutions of a legalistic mentality. Most of us don't realize that legally trained persons, or lawyers, regardless of what other virtues they may have or what other purposes they may serve, are capable, by training, of doing three things. The lawyer is capable of investigating, of defending and prosecuting, and, if he or she gets elected to the bench, of judging. The lawyer uses his training to study the relationship of a particular event, or particular situation, to an existing law or regulation. However, most lawyers do not have the ability, knowledge, or background to initially establish and predicate what those laws should be. They are not primarily trained in technology; they are not trained in economics; they are not trained in social behavior; they are not trained in psychology; they are not trained in all of the areas of fundamental human knowledge that so definitely today affect the behavior and the progress of our society. They can rarely be proactive to ideas; they tend to be reactive to problems.

Philip Hauser, a professor of urban sociology at the University of Chicago, has recently stated (he certainly is not one who has a lawyer's view of the problems in our social institutions) that "the problems which affect American society cannot be resolved without fundamental changes in the law and provisions for the implementation. There is a need to reexamine and revise the law, its content, its nature in terms of twentieth century demographic and technological realities." Neither the so-called liberal or conservative approach is valid any longer. What is required of the twentieth century is an engineering approach that is a resolution of problems and the application of knowledge—not a conservative, liberal, and certainly not an adversarial enactment.

We can no longer afford decisions by politicians or administrative personnel in our corporations, in our government, in our hospitals, and in our schools who have no conceptual understanding, no conceptual ability, no relative training, and no innate confident feeling in dealing with the complexities of our so-called complex society. For the last fifty years, influences for change have come from the knowledge centers and the research institutions of our country. I, for one, believe that the increase in overall well-being in our society did not take the big leap forward when King John signed the Magna Carta, when the Renaissance occurred, when the Reformation occurred, or when the Bill of Rights was written, even though such events were all very major and significant achievements. The real change in the well-being of our society occurred when a large number of people began to walk into laboratories and establish hard knowledge in which many people could have confidence. What this society needs is fewer lawsuits, more cooperation, and more engineering solutions to relieve the roadblocks. We need to replace in much of our government the current legislative and administrative structure and to replace in many of our corporations a large number of politically oriented amateurs who operate without benefit of significant training and experience in a variety of specialized knowledge areas. We need to replace these people with those possessing an appropriate amount of brain power which will emphasize opportunity and tolerable risks, not the expedient solving of problems with risk minimization. Such people should be able to approach their institutions in a disposition of excitement and adventure instead of the regressive and adversarial point of view. They should be able to turn knowledge into progress and thus assure national survival.

In closing, I would like to add a comment by Aleksandr Solzhenitsyn. "I have led most of my life in a society that is devoid of the virtues of any aspect of rational law and to live such a life in such an environment is an intolerable experience indeed. To live life, however in an environment that is primarily governed by rules, regulations and law is a miserable experience also, because it is inconsistent and non-contributing to the spirit of the people whom it designs to serve."

ELEVEN

The Strategic Committee of the Board: A Force for Innovation and Change

AMERICAN INDUSTRY, at least a large segment thereof, has during past decades involved their boards of directors primarily in a variety of perfunctory activities, many required by law, and many involving a skewed emphasis of the specific professional interests of the board members. Such is particularly true when board members are also employed by financial brokerage firms, accounting firms, law firms, and other institutions from whom the corporation may be better advised to buy the services of these representative institutions than involve such representatives on the board itself: much conflict of interest frequently results from the presence of board members with vested interests in their own employer institutions directly able to profit from their involvement with the subject corporation. The usual result of the action of boards so constructed is to be (1) reactive to problems rather than proactive to opportunity, or (2) responsive to short-term legal or financial expedience.

Many boards have also assumed that their only real strategic responsibility is to appoint the chief executive officer and then engage in a relationship with the chief executive that is essentially one of approval and judgment with relatively minor involvement in strategic

Speech given to the Royal Swedish Academy of Engineering Science, Stockholm, and California Institute of Technology, circa 1985.

guidance and motivation—which can be provided *only* by visionary individuals from outside the corporation itself.

A third concept that I believe has limited the overall utility of boards of directors in their service to a corporation is their belief that their only real responsibility is to the stockholders of the institution. Such a limited preoccupation often results in long-term disservice to the stockholders. More useful, I believe, is the concept that the entire corporation's management (including the board of directors) must concern itself with the future of all the *stakeholders:* the stakeholders, a term first used by Stanford Research Institute, include the stockholders, the customers, the employees (including the management), the suppliers, the creditors, the communities in which the corporation operates, society in general, and of course the government (not only that of the United States but apparently those of any country in which the corporation enacts its business)—in other words, any group that has a vested interest in the future and programs of the corporation.

I believe there is little doubt that the board of directors of the American corporation (particularly those involved with dynamic or discontinuous changes in the technology base or marketing profile of the institution) must significantly alter its historically assumed role in the leadership of the corporation; you will note I have said *leadership*, not *management.* I believe the historical inability of the American corporation and its officers and boards to make this distinction between leadership and management is, to a large degree, responsible for the dramatic surprises encountered by American industries—such as the automobile, the basic metals, and to some degree the chemical industries—during the past five years. There have been, incidentally, few events experienced by American industry not predicted by visionaries such as Peter Drucker as long as two decades ago. However, as long as the financial balance sheets, and the straight-line projection thereof, signified future expanding bliss, no cognizance was taken of the approaching "*Age* of Discontinuity."

The proposed new role for the board of directors of a corporation is primarily based on experience I have had with knowledge-based industry, high technology if you prefer, but I do not believe the proposed ideas are limited thereto; they should be applied to any organization who wishes to control its own destiny, by proactively pursuing action motivated by a conviction in its vision of the future—rather than being primarily reactive to the problems delivered to it by its immediate environment.

I believe that the board of directors of a corporation must expand its role in the leadership of the corporation and indeed must assume the primary responsibility for *institutionalizing* that leadership concept and culture within the corporation.

A distinction between "leadership" and "management" is in order. While many people may consider the two terms synonymous in certain respects, I believe it most valuable to draw strong distinctions between the two functions. If we assume effective management is the enactment of procedures that will promote the most effective accomplishment of the activity in which the corporation is now involved, maximize in the most effective manner its current technology, product, market, financial and human resources, we "scope" the usual concept of management horizons normally discussed in the established curricula of our conventional graduate business and management schools. Leadership, as Warren Bennis suggested many years ago, involves the guidance of the organization into those new areas of activity and identity that will characterize the institution at some time in the future, evangelizing what *the future* could be, *and should be,* if the corporation is effectively directed and programmed to accomplish same. Boards of directors cannot become intimately involved in the management function as described above; they can, however, with proper organization, play a vital role in changing the organization to what it should be at some time in the future—by institutionalizing leadership and becoming intimately involved in the innovative programs that will change the organization.

I propose that the board of directors of the corporation become directly involved in the process of innovation and change. Such can be accomplished by forming within the board structure a strategic committee of the board to aid, support, and motivate the inside management of the corporation in the process of innovation—that process of establishing and enacting what the future should and could be.

I. Key Responsibilities of the Strategic Committee of the Board

1. A matching of "impedence" between the corporation and the "outside world."

The strategic committee properly chosen should serve as a window to that ever-changing world of science, technology, changing financial conditions, human resources practices, etc. By bringing into the corporation a diversity of views, exposures, and experiences from other corporations, academic and financial institutions, etc., the strategic committee should improve the flow of outside world intelligence into the corporation, perhaps reducing the barrier of indifference that can infect almost any management that is totally preoccupied with the present business of the institution.

2. Reduce the tendency of management to overindulge and overprotect the vested technology, product, and market interests of the organization.

Professor Louis A. Girifalco of the University of Pennsylvania bluntly states in the January 1983 issue of *Directorship* that "responsibility for dealing with radical innovations should rest with the Board of Directors" because "everyone else in the corporation has a strong vested interest in existing technology. Corporate structure, capital investment, production facilities, and indeed all interests of the firm are closely wedded to existing technology." Corporations must not have overzealous affection for product-market worlds that once served well and are now in terminal demise.

Incidentally, I believe being in the right market with the right product and product technology at the right time is far more significant than any degree of conventional management skill applied to old technology and declining product uniqueness. I doubt if IBM or Du-Pont management skills could do much with the current meatpacking or basic steel business in any reasonable time frame.

3. Institute into the corporation an evident "learner" culture.

Perhaps no characteristic is as important for all members of a corporation to evidence as that of a *learner.* Learners—who hopefully know something as well—are individuals whom others will follow. Knowers who do not display the perpetual openness to learn will not attract or inspire others to change and have little impact on any change or innovation process. A strategic committee of the board (as with any member of management) that displays an intense desire to learn, a perpetual open-mindedness, can indeed be an effective change agent.

When an institution sees key directors in their midst whose curiosity, dedication to learning, and change is apparent, the effects can be dramatic. Management no longer is afraid, as Kettering said, to "fail forward . . . failing forward is a very common methodology of progress."

4. Oversee and cultivate the strategic decision process enacted by top management in major strategic issues.

I am not suggesting that the strategic committee of the board make decisions that management obviously should make. Decision analyses and decision process techniques are becoming highly sophisticated (if not yet totally dependable) procedures and top managements should be coached and encouraged to practice and develop these techniques: only by such practice, and feedback evaluation of the impact of such practices, can the improvement of strategic decision processes be advanced.

5. The direct counseling and advising of top management in major strategic issues such as the corporate technology base, long term product-market policies and directions, human resource policy, financial policies, organizational structure, etc. More will be said about several of these items in later paragraphs.
6. The participation with internal management in the establishment of corporate purpose and major goals and objectives. An example of this responsibility will also be given in a later paragraph.
7. A full participation, with the corporate management, of the process of evangelism of what the company is, where it is going, the purpose of the institution, and the major continuing objectives and goals whose accomplishment signifies "watermark" achievement.

This evangelism can be accomplished in many ways—participating with management in seminars, lecturing by the board members, within the individual expertise of the director, to management or employee groups, or writing in the public media about values and concepts that the employee then recognizes as being promoted within the corporation. As the corporation realizes that the future of the corporation is not the noble dream or temporary whim of one man, the leadership culture will indeed be institutionalized—and as mentioned previously, that is indeed perhaps the major intent of a strategic board committee.

8. The encouragement of corporate management to continuously focus on the purpose of the corporation and be motivated by that wonderful, yet elusive idea of vision without which no purpose will ever be fully achieved—and not be continuously divided or sidetracked by what pragmatists may call "reality."

II. Who Is the Strategic Committee of the Board and How Does It Function?

Any board of any corporation is, we hope, representative of a variety of talents and experiences and an appropriate board is consistent in those talents with the altering needs of the corporation. I believe new talents should be continuously infused into the board as the needs and intent of the corporation changes, and individuals whose abilities are no longer appropriate should be replaced. The strategic committee of the board at any one time should be that segment of the board (perhaps four or five members) whose special unique talents are unusually consistent with the purpose of the corporation, the continuing objectives, and the foreseeable goals under active pursuit.

The concept of the strategic committee of the board can perhaps best be described by considering the initial experiences with the Strategic Board Committee of my own corporation—Lord Corporation. The Strategic Committee of the Lord Corporation board meets separately but as frequently as the total board and usually meets in a location where new stimulation and exposures are possible. It will expose itself to guest lecturers or specialists whose knowledge is presumed to have potentially new strategic impact on the corporation's future. It therefore meets at universities, research institutions, etc. (to date), but there is no reason why it could not meet where the environment will provide the stimulation deemed unique and timely.

The original and current composition of the Strategic Committee consists of:

1. Chairman and CEO of the corporation; he is also chairman of the Strategic Committee.

2. Five other members of the Board of Directors who are:

   - Former vice president of research and engineering of a major high-technology company and now the director of an advanced engineering institute of a major university;
   - a president of a major institute of technology;
   - the CEO of a major industrial corporation;
   - an economist who is president of a major university;
   - a practicing patent lawyer who, among other things, is a practicing entrepreneur involved with a number of ventures.

The president (chief operating officer) of the Lord Corporation is not an official member of the Strategic Committee of the board even though he is a member of the overall Board of Directors of the corporation. The president does, however, attend the board's Strategic Committee meetings when he can. The vice president for planning of the corporation also attends all meetings of the Strategic Committee, serves as meeting secretary, and facilitates communication with an Internal Management Committee of the corporation.

One brief word about the Internal Management Committee of the corporation. This committee, chaired by the president, facilitates the management of the corporation in the sense previously described, managing the current affairs of the corporation in the most effective manner; this committee is composed essentially of the internal officers of the corporation. The chairman and CEO of the corporation *does not* habitually attend the meetings of the president's Internal Management Committee; he does receive feedback from the president and the vice president of planning of the corporation, the latter individual being the one person whose presence at both the meeting of the Strategic Board Committee and the Internal Management Committee is always expected. Indeed, scheduled meetings involving the chairman, the president, and the vice president of planning are the vehicle by which communication and synergism between the Strategic Board Committee and Internal Management Committee are promoted.

It is probably evident by now that we are (1) attempting to place primary but not total responsibility for the leadership of the corporation in the hands of the chairman-CEO with the motivation, guidance, and support of the Strategic Committee of the board, and (2) primary, but not total, responsibility for the management of the corporation into the hands of the president and his Internal Management Committee. Within the context of the definition of leadership and management earlier stated in this paper, this is exactly our intent. It is then the responsibility of the chairman and the president (the Executive Office of the corporation) to make certain that both of these functional efforts are as harmoniously blended and synergized as possible.

III. Some Representative Subjects Considered by the Strategic Committee of the Board

The Strategic Committee of the board has been in operation for approximately one year—having been organized in early 1983 at the suggestion of the overall board itself. During that period of time, the Strategic Committee has been involved in a number of key strategic matters influencing, we believe, the long-term future of the organization.

Perhaps the key and most critical topics involving Strategic Committee consideration have been a critical evaluation and acceptance of the Purpose, Creed, and Mission of the corporation and its operating groups. The Purpose, Creed, and Mission was initially established by the Executive Office with the participation of the International Management Committee.

The following has been taken from Lord Corporation's Corporate Planning Document:

Purpose: *Reason for Existence*
Command a worldwide leadership position by advancing and applying our core technologies to develop, manufacture and market industrial products that assure strong growth and profitability.

Creed: *Philosophy of the Corporation*
We believe in the worth and dignity of each individual and in the need to provide an environment which encourages self-realization of individual potential.

We expect that individuals and organizations will work together to fashion their own destinies and, in the pursuit of excellence, will develop an economy which provides maximum opportunity and freedom.

We pledge that our business will be conducted with integrity and high ethical standards, incorporating a sense of community and civic responsibility which will balance the interests of all our stakeholders.

Mission: *Intended Function in the Economy*

LORD CORPORATION
Achieve our purpose by interrelating the core technologies which are materials science, mechanical dynamics, surface science and active systems to create innovative products of high added value.

MECHANICAL GROUP
Develop, manufacture and market high performance products for the control of mechanical energy to worldwide industrial markets.

CHEMICAL PRODUCTS GROUP
Develop and manufacture sophisticated formulated products and selected chemical and polymer specialties that provide significant added value for customers and market them to worldwide industries that make products from polymeric materials and metals.

INTERNATIONAL GROUP
Expand corporate sales and profits through chemical exports and internationally-based operations when such a physical presence is necessary to facilitate technological interchange and to optimally make and market the products of the Corporation.

The expression of the above Purpose, Creed, and Mission subsequently resulted in the statement and approval by the Strategic Board Committee of seven continuing objectives, the pursuit and achievement of which can directly involve almost all members of the corporation.

CONTINUING OBJECTIVES
1. Provide high caliber human resources for the Corporation.
2. Recognize management's responsibility to manage the Cor-

poration in the proper pursuit of its Purpose, Mission and Creed.

3. Achieve responsible interaction with our stakeholders, including customers, vendors, employees, stockholders and appropriate community, government and academic interests.
4. Develop and acquire new technology and innovative products.
5. Aggressively market technical products and services that provide valuable benefits for our customers and high return to the Corporation.
6. Develop and maintain a strong commitment to quality/productivity improvement.
7. Operate the Corporation at a profit level sufficient to enable accomplishment of all other objectives.

MEASURES OF CORPORATE PERFORMANCE
AGAINST CONTINUING OBJECTIVES

1. Increase corporate sales at least 4% faster than the U.S. industrial economy.
2. Achieve and maintain an average ROA of 12% and a ROE of 18%.
3. Achieve and maintain an earnings-per-share growth of 20%/year.

It is significant that the Strategic Committee, and the overall board itself, does not consider corporate financial performance criteria as objectives in themselves but as measurements of the corporation's effectiveness in fulfilling its objectives. Financial expectancies are not items to which all employees can directly impact or contribute. The expectancy of the Strategic Committee, that we continually and primarily inspect progress made within the domain of Purpose, Creed, Mission, and our continuing objectives, is probably the best insurance that we will achieve those desired financial targets.

IV: Agenda Items for Board Considerations

Four very significant subjects, but perhaps somewhat distinctly separate topics, have been considered by the Strategic Board Committee during its first year of existence. It is assumed that each of these topics will, in time, have its own potent impact on the future of the corporation. In some instances, the Strategic Committee of the board was the innovator of the idea and provided diligent pressure for management action. In other cases the Strategic Committee modified and approved; in others, they approved and displayed an enthusiastic tendency to inspect and audit.

1. The development and maintenance of commitments and programs to quality/productivity improvement. This effort has, incidentally, been of particular concern and subject to proactive push by one of our external Strategic Committee members.

2. Develop and acquire new technology and innovative products. The chairman has perhaps used the Strategic Committee more proactively and aggressively on this topic than he has regarding any subject to date. The result has been the corporate-wide acceptance of four core science and technology areas that will (a) form the basis of research conducted by the corporation, (b) suggest interactive synergism supporting future product development, and (c) form the technology base from which future new products and business thrusts will be forthcoming. The Strategic Committee and corporate management are assisted in this pursuit by a separate Science and Technology Advisory Group, all from outside academic institutions, that reports directly to the Executive Office. This Science and Technology Advisory Committee is essentially concerned with the areas of basic knowledge in which the corporation must continue to expand and become proficient: they are not concerned with products or markets per se.

3. The establishment of a correct corporate model (based essentially on a three "class" system originated by Professor Williams of the Carnegie-Mellon University) has been pursued to allow the appropriate selection of policies, organizations, etc., that are most useful for the model accepted by the corporation—and that will allow the most effective corporate strategy consistent with that model. Professor Williams recognizes three basic types of corporate technology-product-market profiles.

Class I organizations show long product life, have relatively small stable markets where market share is not important, and possess proprietary protection of some type in their product lines. This Class I model is probably most representative of the Lord Corporation at the present time.

Class II organizations are companies that are process-focused, nationwide-marketing oriented, involved in large markets where market share is important, produce standard products, and are usually confronted by three or four major competitors.

Class III organizations are very dynamic, have products of compressed life cycles, demand steep learning curves in all segments of the organization, and have products where the timing and exit of the product into and from the marketplace is critical.

We should not make the mistake of assuming that any one of the classes (I, II, III) is *the* high technology mode. High technology can exist (or not) to some degree or another in all classes: it is almost always present in Class III. If the organization is essentially I, II, or III, or if individual divisions of the corporation are so specifically identified, then research, development, human resources, financial and organizational practices uniquely effective for the model accepted must be pursued. The Strategic Committee, of course, must encourage even radical changes in current practices in the total corporation (or in a selected division) that are of most promising effectiveness.

4. The effect of the Japanese experience in human resources policy, production, and inventory practices, quality assurance practices, etc. is most evident in the model described as Class II and to a lesser extent in Class III.

5. I should mention several topics that are definitely scheduled for consideration in the immediate future. Perhaps the most "enigmatic" subject now facing the Strategic Committee is the nature of fundamental decision processes affecting research and innovation, and the methods by which research planning can be synergized with business plans. The degree and nature of control, specific direction, freedom to explore, degree of planning and projection tolerable in the total innovation process, etc . will be subjects for discussion in the immediate future. How seriously should we encourage the "Skunk Works" scenario—how far should we depart therefrom?

For those to whom the "Skunk Works Tale" is not a familiar household subject, I am referring to Thomas Peters' entertaining yet very provocative dissertation dealing with the process of innovation in a recent issue of *The Stanford Magazine.* "Innovation is unpredictable, it thrives in the chaos of skunk works where product champions go scrounging for success. And, of course, innovation rarely proceeds according to plan." Rejecting either the all dominant importance of the "market plan" or "technology push" myth of product innovation success, Peters forces management to accept a much more opportunistic and creative conduct for new product introduction-based certainly on the likelihood of the correctness of the general technological direction suggested by the corporation's research programs and technology acquisition efforts.

Nowhere does a courageous leadership of a corporation—gambling on the future of research and development that will impact five years to a decade in the future—need more encouragement and support, plus intuitive guidance, from visionary board members than in this area of product innovation and ventures.

As stated earlier, perhaps the major reason for the existence of a Strategic Board Committee is the institutionalization of leadership to give the entire organization the realization that the hopes and vision for the future are the institution's hopes and visions—not those of one man regardless of how influential or significant the hopes and intent of that one man may be. To motivate the entire corporation to follow that institutionalized leadership requires that the organization adopt what Innovation Associates of Boston calls the metanoic viewpoint—namely, "We can create the future" as opposed to "we are bound by current circumstances and realities." The inspired metanoic organization, incidentally, has certain characteristics:

1. It is deeply purposeful and the leadership participates in the discovery of the purpose and vision.

2. It is highly aligned and the leadership catalyzes this alignment around a common purpose and vision, an alignment wherein people freely operate as part of an integrated whole because they see that the purpose of the organization is an extension of their individual purposes.

3. It encourages personal mastery in which the leadership empowers itself and others.

4. It encourages intuition integrated with reason.

5. It encourages people to walk forward and to jump forward but will also accept failing forward.

6. It continuously promotes vision as a guide to effort and conduct

as contrasted to demanding rigorous plans and directions. It makes certain that the vision captures people's imagination and makes the vision feel obtainable.

7. It encourages the pursuit of the vision even when accommodation to current reality appears to be an easier and more comfortable alternative.

I have no doubt that a Strategic Committee of the board, in its primary task of institutionalizing the leadership culture in the corporation, will, in the future, influence the organization in many ways. I doubt if any influence will transcend in importance that of promoting *a vision of the future* as the driving force determining the attitudes and conduct of every stakeholder of the corporation.

TWELVE

Innovation, Not the Making or Managing of Money, Is the Main Challenge before Our Corporate and Government Institutions

America and the Western world will retain its industrial, economic and military preeminence only by a recognition that technological innovation and the entrepreneurial application of new knowledge, obtained through the research and development process, is the primary method by which America and the West has achieved its dominant world position and provided its citizens with an enviable standard of living. That much of our corporate and government leadership does not understand, and has never been directly involved in, the process of technological innovation, may be the "Achilles heel" that will jeopardize our future economic growth and national survival.

Technology—The Primary Agent of Change and Growth

Science and technology, not government action, financial or economic manipulation, or legalistic or philosophical dialectics, are the most powerful agents influencing change in the world today. That any par-

Originally published in *Leaders* Magazine, July–September 1979.

ticular transition may be envisioned as good or bad, moral or otherwise, does not alter this basic fact.

Unfortunately, much of the world leadership, in both its corporate and governmental institutions, does not realize that during the past 200 years—a period during which the human race for the first time in history could hope that tomorrow might be better than today because of wealth creating capabilities of the industrial revolution—science and technology have rapidly become the primary architects of change, human condition and history. We are, of course, still writing history books as though politics and worn out philosophies with their associated dichotomies, are the prime movers in our society. Such have, in reality, become only the noisemakers. The newsmaker events, frequently occurring in the laboratory or on the drawing board a number of years before, are usually not recognized for what they are by the press, the politicians, and often, unfortunately, by corporate executives—in the case of the latter, even when they occur in their own laboratory.

Mankind began his climb out of the slime of misery, disease, early death, and overwork when men in number began working in research laboratories. His continued climb is primarily dependent on his ability to encourage such activity and capitalize on the results thereof. There is certainly a far better correlation between the standard of living and the overall well-being of a society, and the degree to which the fruits of technology have been developed and distributed to that society, than one will find if one correlates social well-being with the form of government or the nature of the political or economic system involved. There are democracies in this world where few Americans or Europeans would desire to live simply because the fruits of technology have not been delivered to the doorstep of the citizens living therein.

Unfortunately, much of the world's existing technological capability is not being effectively utilized to alleviate the world's existing economic deficiencies and social distress. This "information lag"—the discrepancy between what is known and what is practiced is, according to Buckminster Fuller, at the root of the world's failure to solve its poverty, although it is now possible to provide one hundred percent of currently living humanity with the necessary material needs of life. Unfortunately, the people in government who are responsible for the ultimate decisions and policies in our society are, for the most part, not aware of the "information lag."

Also, complaints are often heard by the heads of research of corporations that they have achieved breakthroughs in product or process possibilities that could rejuvenate their industry or company—but that the lack of understanding or feel on the part of the chief executive for the significance of the breakthrough, or the lack of associated entrepreneurial ability on the part of top management prevents further utilization. Such is very common in much of our industrial society, particularly in America and England.

Environment Influencing Technical Innovation

Much has been written regarding the current relative position of American research productivity and American technological strength. Some authors have contended that American research has never been better; others contend that the curtailment of expenditures in behalf of basic research by both government and much of industry spells future disaster for both our economic and military security. I do not intend to herein engage in a discussion regarding the current magnitude of research expenditure or the actual quality of research. I am far more concerned with the environment in which the innovation process must flourish both within our corporations and within those many components of our society directly influenced by legislatures and administrative governmental organizations. Laboratory research can produce extraordinary achievement, and the surrounding environment may be unable to capitalize on the results.

England, for example, over the years has displayed the highest quality of research capability (radar, jet engines, antibiotics, polymeric materials, etc.), but the government, corporate, and social structure of Britain certainly has not been conducive to optimizing these innovations for the unique benefit of the country.

Dramatic Changes in Attitude toward Research

Since 1945 we have witnessed some rather dramatic changes in the attitudes of the American government and the American corporation toward research. Advanced technology then enjoyed unprecedented popularity. Government and industry appropriated large amounts of money for basic research; large segments of government administration and corporate management then waited for the power of research to produce its total magic. These passive observers were frequently disappointed.

In the late 1950s another significant criterion was introduced—research and development must, many managements claimed, be channeled by the stated and evident wants and needs of the marketplace; the marketing executives thereby gained significant power over the selection of research and development activity. History indicates that real new product innovation was rarely the result; product modification or improvement was the normal achievement. The words of Cyril Smith, Institute Professor, MIT, must be heeded: "History shows that technology originated far more often in curiosity and aesthetic urges than in perceived usefulness. Necessity is not the mother of invention—only of improvement!"

The economic recession of the early 1960s witnessed the placement in general executive management of individuals whose backgrounds and training were primarily financial; expenses had to be cut! All too frequently relatively far-out research was the first casualty. What made the situation ridiculous was that basic research is relatively cheap considering the high pay-out when a successful research venture was strategized by competent corporate executive leadership. Why did this happen? In 1951, Irving Langmuir, Nobel laureate and then dean of American industrial scientists, remarked: "The most formidable threat to research and innovation is the growing number of executives and politicians who are making decisions affecting research policy and expenditure, whose training and experience does not permit them to understand what it's all about." Little more need be said.

The Responsibility of Leadership

Carl Prutton, former dean of Case Institute of Technology and later chief research executive in one of America's largest chemical companies, stated, "To realize ultimate utility from research requires comprehension and active participation by top corporate management; general and executive management has greater responsibilities for the end results than does the research manager or the research organization. In this modern era of rapidly changing technologies, when corporate general management is selected, the ability to effectively program research and technology is becoming an absolute requirement." The individuals who guided the growth of high-technology organizations like duPont, Texas Instruments, Hewlett-Packard, IBM, Polaroid, and 3M understood this principle very clearly. Such organizations have been growing at three times the rate of their low-technology counterparts, producing new employment almost ten times as rapidly, improving productivity at twice the rate, and increasing prices only 20 percent as rapidly. Such high-technology companies' products also show a very favorable export trade balance when compared with American industry in general. The economic implications of the ability (or lack of it) of the corporation to innovate, produce, and market products involving new design or production technology are obvious.

Industry in any country must recognize that the basic function of the corporation is to generate new useful knowledge (technology) and move that technology into the marketplace. Only if top management accepts this responsibility will a given corporation continue to serve all its stakeholders (customers, stockholders, employees, and society in general) in a manner that is profitably consistent with each stakeholder's expectations—and with an ability to withstand the onslaught of increasing scientific competence from foreign countries. If corporate leadership fulfills the above described basic function, it certainly will have enacted its primary and fundamental social responsibility, multiplying the totality of the society's wealth, which in a technological society is not a fixed quantity, but a continuously increasing entity.

If science and technology are the most powerful agents of change in our society, and if we are not applying, or controlling, their existing accomplishments as effectively as we might, then we must face the fact that we will need leaders with different types of training and experience than possessed by those who have historically managed the majority of our corporate and governmental institutions. I use the word leader in distinct contrast to the word manager. Many of our institutions are overmanaged and underled. Leadership implies the added ability to conceptualize "what the future could be!" Without this conceptual ability at the top of an organization, the innovation process, through the use of new knowledge, will be seriously inhibited—if it occurs at all.

No one will deny that any organization, governmental or corporate, must be run by individuals with fiscal understanding and responsibility and a sense of legal and moral propriety. Gluck and Foster in their celebrated article "Managing Technological Change: A Box of Cigars for Brad," in the *Harvard Business Review*, clearly point out, however, that preoccupation with current problems, legal matters, financial manipulation and personnel activity now dominate many executives' time, and that they spend little of their day in the development of new product ideas or concepts, or play any significant role in overseeing the technological advance of product line. We need look no further to find the basic reason for the demise of American technological innovation!

Suggestions for Change

A number of dramatic changes must be encouraged in the attitudes of governments, corporations, universities, and society before the revitalization of the innovation process and the unquestioned reestablishment of technological leadership in much of Western society can occur.

1. Government must encourage by its systems of rewards and expectations (at least it must not discourage) the leaders of corporations to accept innovation as their primary responsibility. Government cannot, by its regulations and paperwork, continue to force corporate management to spend most of its time as legalistic umpires and accounting scorekeepers, or assume the role of operating second class welfare agencies. Executives must be deeply involved in the coaching of the innovation ballgame.

2. Corporations and governments must place people in key management positions who at least have a feel for science, technology, and the associated processes of entrepreneurship and innovation. The continued increase of legalistic mentalities, particularly in America, at the top of our corporate and governmental institutions will do little but assure an expansion of the "information gap" discussed earlier.

3. New and innovative educational programs must be enacted in universities and graduate schools of business to continually refurbish

the maturing executive. Most of our management schools in America and abroad are ineffective in educating leaders for technology-based institutions. They primarily emphasize the optimization of conditions within mature product market areas. They do little to kindle the awareness of what the future could be if new technologies are introduced and managed. There are indications that some American universities (and perhaps others) recognize the problem and are instituting new executive technical development curricula.

4. We must establish methods, throughout all countries, of educating the representatives of government to an awareness of scientific progress and technological implication. Perhaps the Swedish Association of Parliamentarians and Scientists might be used as a model for planning. This association has encouraged education programs, field trips, discussions, and other types of communication between the scientific and government community. It is at least a courageous start.

THIRTEEN

Systems Dynamics, Decision Making for the Future

OUR SOCIETY HAS BEEN OPERATING since its inception under the illusion that argumentative and conciliatory techniques in the political process and decision making are the best ways to strategize and enact future programs in social and economic arenas. I believe this is nonsense. We have seen the development over the last 200 years of mathematical and experimental techniques that have produced a dramatic evolution in science, medicine, engineering, etc. These innovations have revamped the oft misguided medieval intuitive methods by which we make decisions that do affect and have affected our lives.

We now have techniques and procedures that allow us to be more farseeing, that are more definite, and are more dependable than the methods by which we now make decisions in our socioeconomic world. The fundamental flaw in our thinking up to this point is that it is based on intuition and debate when our society is so complex that it cannot be reliably analyzed by even the greatest human minds. In fact, most socioeconomic systems are counterintuitive in nature and essentially nonlinear-feedback loop systems. Such systems behave in

Originally published in *Erie & Chautauqua Magazine,* 1993 Annual Business Edition.

a manner completely different from the way "common sense" would predict.

There is a new world in decision making called "systems dynamics," initially developed and promoted by Professor Jay W. Forrester of the Massachusetts Institute of Technology. Dr. Forrester is considered a maverick, as were Newton and Pasteur in their times, but I am convinced that Dr. Forrester will prove to be the Louis Pasteur of the socioeconomic culture and paradoxes of the future.

Dr. Forrester's basic theme is that the human mind is not adapted to interpreting how social systems behave. He finds that evolutionary processes have not given us the mental skill needed to properly interpret the dynamic behavior of the systems of which we have now become a part. Often, the very actions people take to solve difficulties in society are actually the cause of those problems. Well meaning as they may be, people usually do not understand what organizational behavior will result from the complex interconnections of their action. The very nature of the structure of a social system tends to mislead people into taking ineffective and even counterproductive action.

When you consider the great technological advances of the last century, juxtaposed with the relative lack of progress in understanding social systems, the contrast is glaring. Dr. Forrester believes that the reason for the great difference in advancement lies in our failure to recognize that social institutions are, in reality, systems—just as chemical refineries and power plants are systems.

There is a reluctance to accept the idea that families, corporations, and governments belong to the same general class of dynamic structures as physical systems and natural systems, differing primarily in their degree of complexity. We must accept that we, as individuals or as collective groups, are not exempt from the laws that govern the inanimate universe.

A basic fallacy under which our social systems have been and still are being run is that things within that system operate in a simple cause and effect relationship. In reality, our social systems belong to the class called *multiloop nonlinear-feedback systems*. In such systems, the size of the effect is not directly related to the size of the cause, and the cause and the effect are not related by only one path. We must understand that the world does not operate on the basis of what we assume to be the concepts put to us by historical philosophers and theologians, and accept the fact that our intuition is usually wrong and not a valid tool for decision making. Social sciences, says Dr. Forrester, have fallen into some mistaken "scientific" practices which compound man's natural shortcomings. Computers are often being used for what a computer does poorly and the human mind does well and vice versa.

Systems dynamics takes advantage of the powerful system-design methodologies that have evolved over the last fifty years in an approach to designing social systems which combines the strength of the human mind and the capabilities of today's computers. It integrates the theory, methods, and philosophy needed to analyze the behavior of systems in any field. Dr. Forrester has shown that systems dynamics provides a common foundation that can be applied whenever we want to understand and influence how things change through time.

It was the digital computer that allowed Dr. Forrester to develop his revolutionary approach. The process starts from a problem to be solved and puts into play the same kind of testing used in designing an engineering project. Just as everything from spaceships to power plants is designed and tested in laboratories before being put into production, so can realistic models of socioeconomic or any human systems be simulated on a computer. By tapping the wealth of information that people possess in their heads as well as measured data and statistical information, it is now possible to construct in the laboratory realistic models of social systems. A digital computer becomes a simulator, acting out the roles of the operating people in the real system, revealing the behavioral implications of the system that has been described in the model.

The systems dynamics approach starts with concepts and information based on peoples' present behavior, including their ideas and assumptions. Any concept or assumption that can be clearly described in words can be incorporated in a computer model which can then demonstrate the consequences. Usually, these consequences are unexpected, and we learn that the presumed solution to a problem actually exacerbates that problem. Testing possible courses of action first on a computer model can prevent us from taking those ineffective and counterproductive actions which may inflict even more damage on the society we are trying to mend.

Systems dynamics has been lauded by some of the great minds of the modern world. It is being taught even at the high school level in Europe. But it has not yet been recognized in most of the college curricula in the United States. We have been slow to embrace systems dynamics for the same reason that America is slow to embrace any concept or influence which clashes with our short-term mentality. We have become a results-oriented society, geared from childhood to demand instant gratification.

The second law of thermodynamics tells us that any closed system, if left alone, will lose energy and descend into chaos. An insular society eventually will run out of gas. But we can stop the downward spiral by putting some work into our society. Rather than a force to be feared, new information and an openness to new ideas are the energy that keeps society from grinding to a halt.

The systems dynamics approach has been applied successfully to behavior in corporations, internal medicine, fisheries, psychiatry, energy supply and pricing, economics, urban growth and decay, environmental stresses, population expansion and aging, training of managers, and education of primary and high school students. It can give us the opportunities to correct some of society's ills before they become fatal. We must accept that it's time to move into an entirely different system of decision making. Historically, there has been a lag in accommodating to the ideas of visionaries, but we may not have the luxury of waiting too long before revamping our society.

Those interested in positively influencing social or sociological economic environment should study Dr. Forrester's work carefully. It could be our final imperative.

FOURTEEN

The Role of Corporate-Academic Relationships in the Promotion of the Legitimate Purpose of the Corporation

"THE ROLE OF Corporate-Academic Relationships in the Promotion of the Legitimate Purpose of the Corporation" is a subject that has been near and dear to my heart. I was reminded of its critical importance when, several weeks ago, I sat in the office of the president of one of our major Pennsylvania universities and picked up a number of articles on a table arranged for visitors. I found no fewer than four articles concerned with the demise of innovation in American industry. They asked how and why American industry does not have the ability to take new science, new technology, and new engineering breakthroughs and develop new products for world markets (as presumed they once could). This is a concern we, in recent years, have associated with England. We saw the jet engine, radar, polyethylene, Dacron, and many other technological developments succumb to other marketing nations of the world.

Is there a similarity between what has happened in this country and in Great Britain? Perhaps. There are many reasons publicly offered for the inability of the American industrial corporation to develop and introduce new products in world markets.

Speech given as the 1990 Honorary Engineering Lecture at Pennsylvania State University, April 2, 1990, University Park, Penn.

First is the presence of an entrenched, self-serving management culture in our organizations. Louis Lowenstein, Columbia University professor of finance and business, writes in his superb recent book, *What's Wrong with Wall Street,* that the current batch of corporate mavericks attempting to correct this problem by takeover, raiding expeditiously, haven't done American industry much good; in fact, they've done it harm. Professor Lowenstein has done such a superb job of destroying the Robin Hood myth surrounding the likes of Carl Icahn, T. Boone Pickins, James Goldsmith, etc., that I can add little to his presentation.

Second, we often hear of the unprofitable burdening of corporations with expanding social responsibilities, including employee benefits, environmental clean up, public education and support, and so forth. To some extent, such is probably true and is worthy of concern.

I believe, however, the primary reason for the inability of the American industrial corporation to revitalize itself in world markets is the loss of recognition (assuming it was consciously recognized) of the true purpose of the industrial corporation by society and by the people who run it. If corporate managements do not understand their true purpose, they cannot develop workable relationships with universities.

Before I go on, let me tell you what, in my opinion, the American industrial corporation is not. First, it is not an institution with the sole or even primary purpose of maximizing returns to a group of people, who have loaned the corporation their discretionary money as investment but have little knowledge of the basic workings of the organization. About fifteen or eighteen years ago, at a YAMA meeting of the Industrial Conference, the then chair of Union Carbide, Mr. Perry Wilson, predicted that American industry would have great difficulty in perpetually rejuvenating itself because it was rapidly coming under the control of individuals who were more speculators than investors—individuals whose primary interest would rapidly develop into one of short-range perspective without any real concern for long-term survival. Mr. Wilson's major concern at the time was the emerging involvement of industrial pension funds in the stock ownership of the American corporation.

Attempts to treat it as a financial institution, particularly apparent in the USA, can only reduce its effectiveness as a wealth-creating influence for all the stakeholders and the entire social culture involved—an influence that when recognized and adopted suggests strong mutual utility between the industrial corporation and the knowledge-generating academic community. If we persist in looking at and treating the corporation as essentially a financial institution, the corporation's great need, as far as academic talent is concerned, may be limited to the bankruptcy faculty of our law schools.

Second, the American industrial corporation, also, is not a welfare agency with the responsibility to direct and gratify the wants and desires of every citizen. Let's not, as George Stigler, the University of Chicago Nobel laureate, stated, turn the American industrial corporation, the base of the greatest economic force in all history, into a third-class welfare agency. Also, the American corporation is not a resource to pay for the inefficiencies and mistakes of our political institutions. The corporation has enough of its own inefficiencies and mistakes without assuming those of the rest of society. If our corporations are to effectively compete in world markets, they can't be liable for the mistakes and inefficiencies of other components of our society.

We must also consider the realistic nature of the phenomena of competition in our consideration of the true purpose of the corporation, and come to a more meaningful understanding of when it is useful and constructive and when it is self-defeating and contributory to the process of wealth destruction. We equate win-lose scenarios with individual or institutional improvement, rational effort, or long-term survival planning. Of course, win-lose has its handmaid, the preoccupation with the blessedness of competition. Competition, at least in some people's minds, always serves the public. I believe that sometimes it does; sometimes it doesn't. Therefore, the corporation should sometimes be a competitor, sometimes not. I will say more about this subject later in my talk.

Our entire society—corporation and government included—suffers from a so-called information lag—the gap between that which is known and that which is practiced by most of our institutions. This lag, as Buckminster Fuller has claimed, is at the root of the world failure to solve its poverty, although it is now possible to provide 100 percent of currently living humanity with the basic needs of life. The world's great comprehensive universities are a repository of applicable knowledge and, I believe, it is our responsibility as industrial leaders to use this knowledge aggressively for the benefit of our corporations and society. The corporation is not always implementing what it should know to be its purpose.

The Purpose of the Corporation

The true purpose of the corporation is, I suggest, the promotion of a continuous movement of new and useful human knowledge into products, processes, procedures, and services through innovative value-added techniques that enhance a total wealth-creation process and enable the survival of the institution for the benefit of all the stakeholders involved—the customers, the community, the creditors, the employees, society in general, and the stockholders. Indeed, it is the only wealth-creating entity we possess—all others are wealth collecting, wealth distributing, or wealth destroying; this fact alone is probably the reason much of society often treats the corporation as an obvious resource of final resort when the funding of every conceivable community want is involved.

The American government has incidentally acknowledged that the well-being of selected stakeholders is preeminent and has moved mistakenly or unmistakenly to save the corporation. The government didn't bail out Chrysler or Lockheed because it was concerned about the stockholder. They were very much aware of the fact that Lockheed is a repository for technology and engineering and national defense capability. This is the reason that the government bailed out Lockheed. I do not criticize this decision. The primary concern of the government in behalf of Chrysler was certainly not the stockholders, but the employees.

Clever, opportunistic financial exchanging for goods or service, greedy money manipulation, or, as a new culture is now called in the USA by brokerage houses, etc., creative financial engineering are all basically old as legal tender. They have rarely, if ever, succeeded in increasing the power of economic growth, or the size of social wealth in any national entity—and probably never will. As H. L. Mencken once stated, most of our man-created economic problems have, as their basic cause, the desire to get something for nothing and the assumption that such can be done by clever money manipulation or control.

We all respond in reverence to the historical landmarks in the promotion of human rights, like the Magna Charta, the American Constitution, and similar achievements. The fact remains, however, as so eloquently stated by Robert Heilbroner in his book *The Future as History*, that only within the past two hundred years has any significant part of the human race had any hope that tomorrow might be "better than today," at least in the domain of economic well-being and human health. This new era of "hope" is directly related to, and produced by, the Industrial Revolution and the corporations that it has spawned.

The Industrial Revolution produced, of course, some new problems; but the one dramatic effect was the great increase in total socio-economic equity, so that one might hope for, and enjoy, an increase in his or her personal well-being—without the need of taking something from someone else. The Industrial Revolution began a real increase in the "size of the total pie" through the large-scale enactment of "value-added" effects.

There is far better correlation between the standard of living and the overall well-being of a society—with the degree to which the fruits of technology have been developed and distributed to that society—than one will find if one correlates social well-being with the form of government, or the nature of the political or economic system involved.

What do we mean by technology? We mean any useful human knowledge or concept; such certainly not limited to the physical sciences, the biological sciences, or engineering.

Let's take a little adventure into some new concepts that are certainly related to our "Purpose of the Corporation" and show how some enlightened insights may be soon forthcoming and perhaps useful in promoting that purpose.

New Concepts to Aid the Corporation as an Innovator

The chronological life of the industrial corporation—or perhaps more specifically that of each time-evolving technology-product (or process, etc.) market profile within the corporation—can, in accord with Professor Nanus of the University of Southern California, be perceived as passing through three identified phases.

Let's look at these three phases in some detail and see how the ground rules may change as new knowledge is introduced, matures, and, shall we say, "lives out its life."

First, Phase A: A technological phase with economic and social overtones. In this phase, the emphasis is on the development of new products, etc., and on the introduction of those new products and new technology, etc., into the marketplace. The corporation hopefully enjoys, if the new product is really unique, a kind of monopoly that, in some countries, is provided by patent law, to reward and protect the innovator for his or her achievement.

I believe that, in the United States at least, the significance of our patent culture has, during the past twenty years, been greatly underestimated, ignored, and at times chastised by industrialists, the courts, and certainly by schools of business. Patents have not been ignored, however, by the Japanese even within the United States. Fortunately, within the past five years our federal government has established a new Court of Appeals for the Federal Circuit that gives the pursuit, validation, and defense of a patent renewed life.

Edwin Land, the founder of Polaroid, considers the successful defense of his patent culture against Eastman as one of the most significant achievements of his career, because it re-established the value of the patents in the growth of the innovative corporation and in the promotion of the value-added wealth creation process.

Then, secondly, Phase B: A predominantly economic institution with technological and social overtones. During this phase, we encounter a rapid growth of the specific technology-product-market profile both within and outside the corporation. It is probably the period of rapidly increasing capital investment by both the originator and potential competitors. Supply probably still lags demand or perceived future demand. This is the wonderful period of the so-called free market and competition processes that supposedly, to some, always do the greatest good for the greatest number.

It's the phenomena in this Phase B that gave rise to our "sometime" appropriate antitrust laws in America and probably to laws (in the 1930s) prohibiting huge commercial banking and the existence of huge institutional capitalists like J. P. Morgan, who, contrary to popular opinion as Lester Thurow of MIT notes, did not cause the Great Depression, but who possessed both the leadership responsibility and essential ownership of the corporation. We now, instead, have generated an abundance of speculators and traders, not investors who are leaders. A national economy will not profit from this growing trend, either in Phase B or Phase A.

And, thirdly, the corporation is eventually in Phase C: A sociological institution with economic and technological overtones. The transition from the essentially economic Phase B to the essentially sociologic Phase C may be slowly transitional and difficult to specifically identify precisely on the calendar. In this third phase, we essentially encounter aging technology, if not outdated specifically related products, and technology about to be replaced or augmented with a new Phase A.

In Phase C, we probably have a vision of well-established present and future market durability among the technologically uninformed. We are also likely to have (1) many overzealous devices on the part of existing producers to increase market share, (2) new players ready to get in on the act, financial supporters desirous of providing new capital for yesterday's scenarios, and governments all too willing to get more participants into the wonderful world of competitive action—into activity unfortunately soon to be overcrowded with facilities, equity, and investments—an economically wasteful procedure.

We'll likely find an irreversible story of lower prices—that don't always serve the public—falling, and inadequate profit, decreasing service, absorbing of the weaker by the stronger, eventual reversal of the true and useful competition, and perhaps a collapse and premature elimination of a useful product or service. I suspect the American steel industry of the 1950s and the current American telephone and commercial airline cultures may be characterized by an irrational response, by both corporations and government, to activity that had transformed far into the sociological Phase C. We should question seriously in our corporate culture when increased competition serves the public and when it doesn't. Does anyone believe, for example, that increased competition will improve the quality and reduce the cost of health care?

Wise regulation, rather than unbridled competition, is probably more appropriate for the sociological phase of corporate activity, if that product or service is a vital need or right—and not just a want. No society should be encouraged to put extensive new investment in technology old to its culture.

Incidentally, Robert Augros and George Stanciu, the former a philosopher and the latter a physicist, have in their recent book, *The New Biology,* seriously questioned the Darwin concept, that in nature all organic beings are exposed to severe competition and to the universal struggle for life, a paradigm that has dominated biology since Darwin's day. In fact, modern biologists believe that competition is not as common as assumed, that nature employs many strategies to avoid competition, that synergistic cooperation is far more common, and that the stabilizing cooperation that appears to eventually dominate may indeed be proceeded by a useful, but transitory competitive phase. A win-lose culture is not always dominant in nature.

A simple example may illustrate the foregoing concepts. The man who invented and patented the gasoline pump and erected a service station to assist the automobile owner did him a great service (Phase A); the appearance of the second pump on the opposite corner (Phase B), at the appropriate time, also may have positively affected the neighborhood—maybe by just keeping the inventor responsible; the addition of a third station may be economically and socially questionable; and a fourth inexcusable—the public will eventually suffer.

Government, corporations, and inventors should realize that laws, regulations, judgments, etc. that are useful and appropriate for Phase A, or B, or C may be totally useless, counterproductive, or even disastrous when applied to the other phases. Governments, investors, creditors, and corporate leaders should recognize these realities and not assume that a given technology-product-market world is a homogeneous culture, but that it has well-defined chronological identities, each of which must be treated by distinctly different policies and distinct legal, financial, and accounting procedures. Perhaps we should broaden and define an expanded conceptual awareness of what we mean by a useful "Bottom Line"; such may change and depend on phase and time. Why do we assume that the owner of common stock of a company have total freedom to do with the future of an industrial organization whatever they believe will serve their limited interests? Most of us do not have that freedom to dispose of any of our possessions, and that action has a strong negative effect on the rest of society.

Dr. Douglas Bond, a psychiatrist and former dean of the Case Western Reserve Medical School, stated many years ago that laws, expressed principles of economics, and other factors determining economic decisions must distinguish between human hopes, human wants, and human needs or rights (incidentally, these roughly correspond to the Phases A, B, and C of this discussion). We must also realize that a need in one society may not yet even be a "hope" in another.

Corporate/Academic Relationships

How does all this relate to corporate-academic interrelationships? Much of the understanding of the phenomena cited above is being generated in academia and, like the fundamentals of chemical reaction mechanisms, solid state physics, transport theory, or the new domains of artificial intelligence, such awareness should be utilized for the maximizing of opportunity (and the solution of problems)—unless we foolishly enjoy the unbridled growth of the "information lag" described above.

A most confusing problem that exists in the corporate culture, at least in America, is either our inability or unwillingness to recognize the difference between sound long-range economic data and programming, and what is often short-sighted financial tabulation and numbers (often demanded, I'll admit, by an atmosphere of speculation and trading). Effective long-term investment and opportunity maximization (at a tolerable but not minimal risk) is not served by such confusion. In America, we are plagued with a dearth of real capitalists—real entrepreneurs—wishing to invest their time, money, and life intent to promote and prove an idea through Phases A and B. Our so-called operating statements and balance sheets, following what we call "accepted accounting procedure," certainly do not reflect institutions consciously operated for the benefit of all the stakeholders—nor do they distinguish among Phases A, B, and C. Many of our conventional procedures for cost management, for example, are more likely to produce, as Professor Bitran of MIT states, lose-lose propositions. John

Campi, an accountant at Parker-Hannifin Corporation in the USA, states his profession has failed to fulfill many of its responsibilities. His boss, Chair Patrick Parker states, "In today's environment, we don't think numbers tell the real story. For example, we all know how to put a figure on losing our customers, but you can't put one on our successful efforts to hold them."

I suspect that our new world of computer-aided manufacturing, specific in intent when it started, may have a major added benefit, that of emphasizing the inadequacy of our current financial approaches and systems in the enactment of capital investment and operation decisions affecting long-term economic growth. Most of our current manufacturing cost systems, for example, emphasize much trivia, underweight factors of great importance, and totally ignore influences appropriate to a given technology-product-market phase (A, B, or C) or concern for the future of all the stakeholders.

Unfortunately, as stated earlier, most "accepted accounting procedures" designed primarily (certainly in the United States) to produce information for the propagation of a cyclical twelve-month tax system do not even attempt to add new or encourage decisions that would accommodate a "stakeholder" perspective, or recognize the necessity of additional investment perspectives that would distinguish among our Phase A, B, and C domains.

If new and useful human knowledge is vital to the promotion of the proposed basic purpose of the industrial corporation, then it should be obvious that a major source of that knowledge is the organization that is open to all—the university or academic institutions of higher learning. We should assume that any of the phases (A, B, or C) are vulnerable to the continuous introduction of new knowledge.

If we are to promote the suggested basic purpose of the corporation, it should also be obvious that we need more long-term leadership perspective, in contrast to the conventional managerial habit inherent in many of our corporations. This managerial culture has historically dominated the mentality of our graduate schools of business, and concerns itself more with making current product market activity more effective or efficient; the managerial culture certainly has done little to understand or stimulate Phase A activity.

Many American corporations that are succumbing to the current pressures of short-term money speculation are overmanaged and underled, leadership being that visionary ability to guide the organization through a period of constructive destabilization necessary as the organization envisions what "the new exciting future could be."

Science and technology and new knowledge—not government action, financial manipulation, or legalistic dialectics—are the most powerful agents influencing change in the world today. That any particular transition may be envisioned as good or bad, moral or otherwise, does not alter this basic fact.

Unfortunately, the people both in corporations and in government who are responsible for the ultimate decisions and policies in our society are often not aware of the mentioned information lag produced by the rapid generation of new knowledge and our institutions' inability to use the same.

Complaints are often heard by the heads of research of corporations that they have achieved breakthroughs in product or process possibilities that could rejuvenate their industry or company but that the lack of understanding or feeling on the part of the chief executive for the significance of the breakthrough, or the lack of associated entrepreneurial ability on the part of top management, prevents further utilization. Such is very common in much of our industrial society.

England, for example, over the years has displayed the highest quality of research capability (radar, jet engines, antibiotics, polymeric materials, etc.), but the government, corporate, and social structure of Britain certainly has not until recently been generally conducive to optimizing these innovations for the unique benefit of the country.

In 1951, Nobel laureate Irving Langmuir remarked, "The most formidable threat to research and innovation is the growing number of executives and politicians who are making decisions affecting research policy and expenditure, whose training and experience does not permit them to understand what it's all about." Little more need be said.

Carl Prutton, former dean of Case Institute of Technology, stated, "To realize ultimate utility from research requires comprehension and active participation by top corporate management; general executive management has greater responsibilities for the end results than does the research manager or the research organization. In this modern era of rapid-changing technologies, when corporate general management is selected, the ability to effectively program research and technology is becoming an absolute requirement." The economic implications of the ability (or lack of it) of the corporation to innovate, produce, and market products involving new design or production technology are obvious.

Suggestions for Change

A number of dramatic changes must be encouraged in the attitudes of governments, corporations, universities, and society before the revitalization of the innovation process and the unquestioned reestablishment of technological leadership in much of Western society can occur.

1. Governments and corporations must encourage, by systems of rewards and expectations, the leaders of corporations to accept innovation as their primary responsibility.

2. Corporations and governments must place in key management positions people who at least have a feel for science, technology, and new knowledge and the associated processes of entrepreneurship and innovation. The continued increase of legalistic mentalities, for example, at the top of our corporate and governmental institutions will do little but assure an expansion of the information gap, discussed earlier.

3. New and innovative educational programs must be established in universities to continually refurbish the maturing executive—maybe new types of schools, including unique business schools, law schools, and advanced technology and training institutions are needed. Most current management schools are certainly ineffective in educating leaders for technology-based institutions. They primarily emphasize the optimization of conditions within mature product market areas. They do little to kindle the awareness of what the future could be if new technologies are introduced and promoted.

4. We must establish methods, throughout all countries, of educating the representatives of government to an awareness of scientific progress and technological implication. Perhaps the Swedish Association of Parliamentarians and Scientists might be used as a model for planning. This association has

encouraged educational programs, field trips, discussions, and other types of communication between the scientific and government community. It is, at least, a courageous start.

5. And we must, as industrialists, enact an enhanced aggressive familiarization with the basic knowledge-creating organization of our society—the university. We must also support it with an increased amount of our time and money.

6. Thirty years of various forms of contact with academia have suggested to me the following options for the involvement of a corporation with the university culture.

   - Broad-scale "shopping" type exposure of the corporation to the academic world. Industrial personnel must aggressively pursue such liaison and continuously survey wide areas in science, technology, and knowledge, analyzing and synthesizing the results of academic research as stimulations and suggestions to "what is possible," for example, to improve the corporate technology-product-market futures.

   - The pursuit within academic institutions of "target" individuals or departments whose high prominence or expertise are well established and obviously pertinent to the existing interests of the corporation.

Effective innovation in the technology-based company certainly requires an expanded association between the academic world and the corporation. This association cannot, however, be highly effective if it is perceived to be totally the domain of a few curious, aggressive scientists and engineers from the industrial firm. General management and corporate management must be involved with their support and understanding and, far more than in the past, with their presence in the academic environment. They must become as comfortable shopping and buying in the academic environment as they are elsewhere. The entire industrial corporation must be transformed into a dynamic learner culture.

1. We must, as industrialists, recognize that the major responsibility for utilizing the productivity of the knowledge-

generating institutions, for the benefit of our corporations, is ours (not academia's). As Professor Rustum Roy of Penn State says, "University-industry coupling of all kinds: consortia, centrals, affiliate programs, etc., are all the rage." True, and the ways in which industry can relate to the university are varied, and the techniques multiply daily. In my own company, I've counted no fewer than eighteen methods often enacted through twenty-three academic institutions, but the key to making them work is top executive involvement that is intent on promoting the true purpose of the corporation.

2. Finally and again, we should not assume that the only useful kind of knowledge forthcoming from our universities is knowledge from the hard science, engineering, or conventional economics and management cultures.

Examples for Change

Several months ago, the Lord Foundation of Massachusetts gave awards for innovation to six distinguished individuals: Nobel laureate James Watson, of double helix fame; Isaac Asimov, the writer; James Buchanan, the Nobel Prize winner for economics; Professor Jay Forrester, the father of systems dynamics; Professor Herman Mark, the grandfather of polymer science; and Dr. Edward Land of Polaroid. During speeches by these gentlemen and other academics, three concepts or ideas were presented that I, as an industrialist, plus my colleagues in industry and members of our government had better understand if we in industry are to grow in effectiveness and enact our true corporate purpose.

1. According to Professor Buchanan, the so-called work ethic—that is, the basic personal desire to work—is deeply embedded in the human psyche. It is not just a vehicle of survival, and it does contribute implicitly a value-added dimension to our economic growth; it also represents a true economic force in the wealth-creation process—a process that produces a spillover benefit for all. Such force and effect, Professor Buchanan believes, may be neutralized by the

leisure-time syndrome growing in Western society. The basic psychological will to work may be a vital component of any future economic theory.

2. Professor Lester Thurow stated that "America can no longer provide an adequate support structure for its truly innovative people, and our inability to compete in world industrial markets is to a large degree due to this fact. Two reasons exist for this difficulty: (1) Our decreasing ability to train a highly literate work force because of the ineffectiveness of our secondary school systems and (2) our unwillingness or inability to train and engage skilled personnel for our manufacturing operations, primarily because of the low prestige and reward culture we associate with people who may, whole or in part, work with their hands and their backs." I agree with Professor Thurow. We seem to socially esteem any level of competency in behavioral and misbehavioral scientists (the latter is Jacques Barzun's word for artists) more than we do skilled craftsmen, like good plumbers. As noted by John Gardner, such will guarantee that neither our ideas nor our pipes will hold water.

Conclusion

In closing, I must mention that amazing, provocative, and still essentially academic world of Professor Jay Forrester's system dynamics. According to Forrester, "Our socioeconomic systems (management, environmental, politics, economic behavior, medicine, etc.) are counter intuitive in their nature and are, to the analyst, multi-loop feedback systems. They are not subject to effective understanding, design, and control by conflicting opinion, committee meetings, and compromises—all mostly acting without any dynamic analysis adequate to prevent unexpected consequences; in fact, we often get the exact opposite of what we desire." This system's dynamic discipline, I suspect, will revamp the methods by which we design our corporations, make industry and government decisions, and more effectively program our resource allocation for total stakeholder benefit.

Forrester and his systems dynamics will in the future, I believe, create a revolution in the way we manage our society and its organizations, including corporations—a revolution as dramatic as Pasteur's disturbing (and opposed) theories for the treatment of disease that appeared eighty years ago. This new Systems Dynamics discipline alone is sufficient to hurry all of us to the halls of academia with an open mind and computer in hand.

The corporation can be a vital force and constructive example for all society as it carries out its true purpose which displays a dedication to support the generation, dissemination, and utilization of new knowledge for the benefit of all the stakeholders. In partnership with academia, the enlightened corporation can lead the world to win the race between education and knowledge on one hand and catastrophe on the other.

FIFTEEN

Lord Corporation's Greatest Generation

TOM BROKAW'S BOOK, *The Greatest Generation,* describes the lives and pursuits of American citizens during the World War II era. I would like to include in that "Greatest Generation" the many employees of Lord Corporation who worked not only during World War II but also through the Depression, the Korean War, the Cold War, and the Vietnam Conflict. These employees are the men and women who shaped our company with the continuous and constructive values of ethics, morality, and strength.

Unfortunately, over the last two decades, the era of American social and economic enlightenment that our employees envisioned has not occurred. This period has instead been tainted with greed, the pursuit of entertainment, and fashionable retirement. A faculty member from the University of Hawaii recently stated, "This is not the age of information, it's the age of entertainment." Can anyone disagree with that analysis?

In 1970, Professor Leonard Read, from the Foundation of Economic Education, wrote a book entitled *Coming Aristocracy.* Read's aristocracy was one whose primary concern was the pursuit of excellence. This meant doing the best job that you knew how to do in your life's work. The continued growth of knowledge in one's life was the key to one's maturity—a maturity that promotes liberty and the work ethic, instead of a fashionable lifestyle.

Speech given at the Lord Quarter Century Club, August 25, 2001, Erie, Penn.

This definition of aristocracy assumed self-responsibility, individuality, and self-respect. The loss of self-respect, self-discipline, and self-control leads to much of what society now endures—riots, crime, and other irresponsible actions.

"Many people speak of faith, hope, love, and charity, but of these qualities," Karl Menninger said, "the greatest is hope—hope that tomorrow will be better than today for all of us."

Such hope is a fairly recent vision for humanity that actually started with the Industrial Revolution. This economic revolution increased the size of the economic pie, allowing it to be peacefully divided among many instead of taken forcibly by a few. Unfortunately, what was envisioned in the book *Coming Aristocracy* did not occur and a full measure of "hope" for most Americans was not forthcoming.

In the media and our conversation, we have too often emphasized the word *rights* when we should have spoken of *responsibility*. Additionally, instead of the word *freedom*, maybe we should have emphasized the word *liberty*, which means *freedom* plus *responsibility*. Incredibly, the word *freedom* doesn't appear in the Constitution, but *liberty* does.

Perhaps we need to use the word *work* more often instead of *opportunity*, and *duty* more often than *entertainment*. In a recent conversation with former Chief of Staff Colin Powell, I used the word *duty* and Powell remarked, "I haven't heard the word *duty* since I retired from the Army."

Suppose we speak more of our *efforts* and less of our *rewards*, and work toward the acquisition of *knowledge* instead of acquisition of *portfolio*. I'm not suggesting these words needing deemphasis are not good, but I think they are overexpressed at the expense of those words that would ensure the conduct, values, and behavior that will produce real accomplishment and survival of our society. In addition, we might try using *fairness* instead of *justice*—and perhaps place more emphasis on *cooperation* and less on *competition* as noted by Robert Alexrod's classic text, *The Evolution of Cooperation*.

Many authors like W. Edwards Deming have stated the growth of American industry has occurred not because of competition but in spite of it. I believe competition is useful in dealing with *wants*—when a man can keep his money in his pocket until he wants to spend it. On the other hand, when we're dealing with *needs*, I don't feel competition is nearly as effective in serving humanity as we've been asked to believe. Do you believe competition will serve us better in our health care or educational efforts?

How about using the words *win-win* instead of *win-lose* in our activities? We should perhaps speak of long-term *effectiveness* instead of *efficiency*. How about *purpose* instead of *profit*? How about understanding instead of *agreement* or *disagreement*? Why don't we talk about *stakeholders* in a company instead of *stockholders*? Stakeholders, of course, include employees, customers, suppliers, management, stockholders, and the government. Incidentally, the most important stakeholder in a company depends where it is in history. If it's wartime, your most important stakeholder is the government's Department of Defense.

For those employees who have a large part of their occupational career ahead of them, I believe your greatest contribution to your corporation is made when you ask, "What can I do for this company?" instead of "What can this company do for me?" Peter Drucker, a behavioral economist and corporate leader, identifies three people who qualify under this statement: Jack Welch, recently retired CEO of General Electric; George Marshall, who came out of retirement three times to serve his country; and Harry Truman, who consistently placed his country over himself.

The '50s, '60s, and '70s provided great learning in the field of institutional management and leadership. This learning was led by such notables as Drucker, Warren Bennis, Douglas McGregor at MIT, F.J. Roethlisberger and Abraham Zeleznik at Harvard, Rensis Lickert at Michigan, Cris Argyris at Yale, Crawford Greenewalt at duPont, Ralph Cordiner at General Electric, and Frederick Kappel at AT&T. Too much of the pioneer vision of these giants has been shelved while pursuing countless numbers of tactical whims and follies. Unfortunately over the last twenty years, we've forgotten that knowledge is more durable and valuable than paper wealth.

Professor Herman Daly, of the University of Maryland, has written several books where he states his opposition to values based on our current outmoded accounting system that puts dollar values on outdated inventories, but ignores employees, human intelligence, the organization, and intellectual property.

I recall a conversation with economics professor James Buchanan of the George Mason University, who was also a recipient of the Lord Symposium Award in 1988. I asked Buchanan, "Suppose one morning, everyone woke up with one million dollars in their wallet. The first thing a typical guy would do is say, 'Hey, I'm, through working. I'm quitting my job and we're all going on vacation!' Well, when he got to the grocery store for supplies, he'd find it closed because everyone who worked there would've quit their jobs as well. And there would be no one at the gas station either because they'd all gone fishing. So let's assume that everyone who felt secure in their newly gained million dollars quit working. What do you think that million dollars would be worth at the end of the day? Zero!"

Buchanan laughed and said, "Everything in your savings depends on the fact that people in the future are going to work. Your money, stock, and bonds are basically 'IOU's' from the future workforce to you that state someone is going to work to assure that your investments have value."

Finally, may I leave you with these thoughts—Whether you're are a foreman, laboratory manager, or new employee, there are characteristics of all managers and leaders that are most worthy. These are the essence of corporate leadership and managerial trust.

First, according to Crawford Greenewalt, former president of du-Pont, are good manners. Second, an honest concern for the people around you and what happens to them. This goes beyond superficial greetings or the traditional box of candy at Christmas. Third is a sense of humor—the kind where you can laugh at yourself and admit your mistakes, but not the kind that pokes fun at others. Forth, one must be a learner and listener—especially to those people around you who no doubt know more than you about a subject. It's amazing how listeners and learners are *listened to* and *learned from* more readily by other employees. Fifth, one must be able to delegate and hold his or her employees responsible while giving them latitude to perform. Sixth, have the ability to tolerate risk; good planning is maximizing opportunity at a tolerable risk.

The most important of all managerial qualities is total human honesty. If one is ever deemed as being dishonest, it's very difficult to ever restore confidence in their audience. Being totally honest is the best way to stay out of trouble and eliminate the necessity of telling more lies to cover up the initial one.

Maybe I'll get to talk to you again sometime, maybe not. But I hope you have a pleasant day and a safe journey to your destination. Thank you for listening.

The American Corporation and Its New Dilemma: Costly Health Care of Inadequate Quality

MUCH HAS BEEN WRITTEN regarding the importance of the quality of education at all levels, to the general industrial and economic health of the United States. We realize as a nation that we much dramatically improve the delivery of higher intellectual capability to our citizenry at an improved cost/benefit ratio. America spends more money per student, with disappointing results, than does Japan, Germany, or Switzerland. We can, I believe, recognize that there are basically two reasons for this ineffectiveness. The first problem is (1) the so-called information lag, first identified as such by Richard Kostelanetz in the book *Beyond Left and Right* as that *gap* between which is now known and/or productively practiced *somewhere in the world* and that which is unknown within the culture in need of change. The second problem is the unwillingness of our society to make tough decisions or changes, even when there is no "gap," change without which little improvement is likely. Both the "gap" and "willingness" factors deter improvement in American public education. Unless dramatic change in the quality of American education occurs both intrinsically and in cost/benefit ratio, the American corporation

Draft of a speech prepared February 28, 2007.

will be required to make dramatic changes if it is to survive, perhaps, for example, in the distribution internationally of facilities.

Now American industry is confronted with another major problem in cost/benefit analyses, perhaps as acute as the access to a literate, educated population—that of high-quality health care for its employees. Americans work more hours to pay for a given medical service than do the Europeans or Japanese—and all too often receive a quality health care well below that possible in view of existing knowledge or the size of any information gap. Why?

We are all aware of the continuing discussion about HMOs, rising medical *costs*, malpractice insurance, etc. Has anyone, however, asked about the *quality* of health care corporate employees receive? Quality expressed in terms of a rapid solution to a patient problem by procedures that effectively bring to bear the totality of existing knowledge in the shortest possible time interval, not in terms of morbidity or mortality "outcome effectiveness." Unfortunately and unnecessarily, the many corporate employees in the United States are not receiving adequate health care and such inadequacy is not necessarily because of a lack of competent—and in *many cases* highly competent—physicians. Why? It is, I believe, because the medical profession's long established system for the delivery of that health care is no longer a viable culture in a world of increasing attention to treat complex maladies and an aging population. Quality health-care delivery demands that, above all, as in any other diagnosis and delivery of product or service within the limits of existing human knowledge, it be done *right the first time.*

The American health-care system is essentially set up like an obstacle course plagued with time delays and frustration for the consumer. The major stumbling block is that, with few exceptions, doctors function as independent, unregulated, entrepreneurial businesses. Yet doctors in private practice can be really anything but independent. They are, if competent, extremely dependent on the expertise of other physicians and the medical facilities of an institution. If a person's illness requires more than a basic examination and treatment, the typical doctor's office probably does not have the equipment, staff, laboratories, or specialized expertise to fully treat the patient; hospital-type facilities must be used. The patient is referred to a series of tests (some enacted because of fear of malpractice suits or because some physicians have financial interest in the service), examinations, and appointments stretched out over several weeks—and, in some cases months, often carried out in different locations. This "tandem exposure" of the patient to a series of fee-oriented entrepreneurs essentially prevents the probability that quick adequate diagnosis and initial quality treatment be enacted in a short period of time.

This "tandem" referral process is a primary area where the medical profession's current system appears most inadequate. It is a marked barrier to achieving a most significant characteristic of any quality process of diagnosis, treatment, or design—*that of doing it right the first time,* whether you're correcting problems in a jet fighter or a human body.

To illustrate the point, suppose a patient has a complicated illness and eventually needs to see four specialized physicians: a general practitioner, a nose and throat specialist, a pulmonary specialist, and a neurologist. If the typical patient makes an appointment with his general practitioner, how much time would probably lapse before the person saw all four physicians? One or two days? The odds of winning the lottery are better. One or two weeks? Possibly, but that's probably the minimum. Three to six weeks? This is more common, but don't bet on it. Six to eight weeks? Generally, a person must make appointments with individual practitioners who are booked weeks in advance, arrange for baby sitters or time off work, make at least four separate trips, and actually undergo separate consultations or examinations by one general practitioner and three physicians over an extended time period. Meanwhile, the patient remains uncomfortable, untreated, and uncured—unlike the problem with a sick jet fighter, the patient's condition does not remain static but probably deteriorates!

Furthermore, after the patient has been examined in tandem, over an extended period of time, by all four physicians, what are the chances of the physicians meeting collectively to discuss the patient's symptoms and reach a consensus on the illness, cause, and recommended treatment? More likely, the results are accumulated by one of the physicians who makes a final determination—based on tests, or discussion, or records many weeks old. Appropriate real-time communication between varied expertise really cannot occur with this type of scenario. Anyone engaged in the analysis and subsequent action involving *any* complex physical, biological, or biophysical system is well aware of the validity of this statement.

If a person is critically ill, the process can be shortened, but only if *a* particular physician deems necessary. The patient, subjected to this quagmire of time delays, has no control over the doctor's schedule or a hospital or lab's facilities—*indeed there is usually no institutional culture that has real control or responsibility in time schedule or decision quality over the diverse inputs of varied expertise.*

To further illustrate the ineffectiveness of the current health-treatment system, consider the same scenario projected artifically in the relationship between an automotive supplier and a major automaker.

The automaker (the patient) goes to its supplier (the doctor) to resolve a problem it's having with door hinges on its luxury sedans. The automaker makes an appointment with the supplier to discuss the problem. One of the supplier's representatives meets with the automaker, discusses the problem, and then tells the automaker to see his metal fastener specialist in two weeks at another facility. After meeting with this first specialist, the automaker is told to make an appointment in three weeks with the supplier's metallurgist. The metallurgist probably enacts a series of extensive tests at some laboratory in which he may have a financial interest or partnership. These tests, often done in excess, also serve to protect the metallurgist from his version of a malpractice suit. Incidently, the supplier's initial representative and the metal fastener specialist have probably submitted bills to the automaker who has not yet seen the metallurgist and, of course, little or nothing yet has happened that eases the expectancies of the automaker.

The business relationship ends right there! No, it probably would have ended within the first week. Why? Because the automaker—like the patient—has a problem now, not two or five weeks from now, and will not compromise its well-being by waiting for a supplier to find the appropriate procedure time to help resolve the automaker's problem. Instead, the automaker finds a supplier who understands that the automaker is its customer and the *sole reason* for its existence. Any acceptable supplier (i.e., a hospital) should organize every and any bit of available expertise in his organization within forty-eight hours.

Continuous improvement is now keeping the auto industry striving for quality and effectiveness. I emphasize continuous improvement —not competition. The effectiveness of the latter (competition) depends on whether we are dealing with a human need or a human want. Society's inability (particularly its accountant, economist, politician, and lawyer) to distinguish between these concepts is one of the reasons why "competition" has questionable utility to the delivery of health care. But what motivates the medical profession? Malpractice suits? Perhaps, to some extent control by the conventional community hospital. But private doctors operating on a fee basis essentially don't respond to any significant degree to any institutional influence or control. Most are independent professionals often with *strong moneymaking orientation.* So if patients are left in limbo for several weeks with a debilitating illness, who can the patient turn to? Usually in most of our community hospitals really no one with the power and dedication to really act. There is rarely any institutional influence possessing the combination of responsibility and authority, that is obvious to the patient, dedicated to the patient's well-being and the institution's reputation—certainly like any customer expects to find in most corporations.

What is an alternative?

Secondary or tertiary care clinics, such as the Mayo Clinic, the Cleveland Clinic, Johns Hopkins, etc., are more likely to have systems structured to treat their patients timely and effectively. The basic culture of such CLINIC is that the physicians are usually employees on salary, not individual fee-oriented entrepreneurs.

Such a clinic or hospital (for the sake of brevity, I'll call them CLINICS) like the average community hospital is staffed with physicians many of whom specialize in a variety of disciplines (probably more so). Unlike most communities, the physicians at CLINICS are salaried and work for the CLINIC. Patients are treated by the CLINIC's coordinated staff, not a series of independent entrepreneurs. The patient who needed to see a general practitioner and three specialists typically would be able to see all of them quickly—maybe the same day, depending on the length of the examinations. This timely aggregation of specialization is enacted by the CLINIC's culture. Since the physicians work for the CLINIC, they are there every day to see the CLINIC'S patients, unlike private physicians who rotate between several hospitals and offices. Again, it is part of the CLINIC'S culture that the physicians at the CLINIC do meet together quickly and *in person* to discuss a patient's case, since they are at the same facility at the same time.

At these CLINICS, the operative mind-set is, "This is *our patient*, and we will treat our patient at our CLINIC." The operative mind-set of most of the private physicians' community is, "This is *my patient*, and I treat my patients at *this hospital*." I know, I have had board responsibility at both types of institutions. The difference is that a CLINIC is equipped to provide comprehensive medical care for most illnesses in a timely, efficient manner, that attempts attention *as an institution* to do it "right the first time." A private fee-oriented doctor or, series of such, is not.

Companies that are tired of seeing their employees receive inadequate care, while their medical costs continue to rise, are finding CLINICS an attractive alternative. Incidentally, a company I know in Baltimore required all employees who needed inpatient care for a nonemergency illness to go to Johns Hopkins Hospital. The company's medical costs *went down* 30 percent and the level of quality care employees received improved. The reason, the CLINIC is more likely to *Do It Right the First Time.* Costs went down because the quality of care went up. It is often the improper original diagnosis, with its effect being that the person's illness prolongs or worsens while waiting for correct diagnosis and treatment, which produces extensive cost and expense; such is far more expensive than a correct initial diagnosis procedure *even if* the initial "round" was more costly.

In any system, whether in the medical profession or in manufacturing industry, one of the keys to quality is to remove barriers that prevent improvement. To provide a quality product and service and initiate procedures that promote a quality environment, an organization must continuously improve its operations or services and the management of the organization must be the vanguard leader. The current doctor/hospital system in most communities with its inherent fee-oriented physician mentality, and the My Patient—This Hospital mind-set, is the dominant institution culture, is a large barrier to improving the health care in this country and subsequently reducing health-care costs. In any human activity—whether it's health-care delivery, legal service, the design of an industrial product or process, etc.—intent of *doing it right the first time always* is paramount and such results in higher quality and lower costs and greater customer satisfaction.

Fortunately or unfortunately, depending on your viewpoint, the future of health care in this country (because of the increased complexity of both human illness and treatment) will, I believe, demand an entirely different relationship between an institution and its medical staff—whether that institution is a primary, secondary, or tertiary care center in Boston, Erie, Pa., Terra Haute, or Poodle Junction. That relationship must, I believe, move more toward the physician-institution relationship being one of employee-employer. Whenever a salary replaces a fee and where competency is rewarded or incompetency rectified by the employee's peer evaluation and also expected and enacted by the institution, higher quality will prevail and costs will be reduced; the responsibility for malpractice defense would also then rest with the institution, with an enhanced objectivity on the part of the physician. Historically it is obvious that health-care delivery has, in America and perhaps elsewhere, functioned primarily with the a priori convenience of benefit to the physician as a first priority—not that of the customer.

There is one other dramatic advantage to the movement of the health-care delivery system to the institution-employee culture and the salary review action based on competence and performance. We may begin to rid the medical profession of many physicians whose motives are to a large degree based on greed and immature unbridled desire for unmanaged freedom and who resent being evaluated by an organization staffed and structured by their competent peers.

The corporation has, of course, a number of alternatives to follow to reduce the costly human and financial effects of the current inadequate health care system:

1. It can encourage employees to go to appropriate CLINIC facilities by, for example, placing limits on time or money on the treatment of a complex illness in the community hospital or within the tandem-fee culture.

2. It can decentralize internationally to other industrial western countries.

3. It can establish, within the areas of its major operations (with perhaps the cooperation of other companies), strategic diagnostic facilities to guide and direct its employees for treatment to CLINICs wherein greater probability exists for "Doing It Right the First Time."

Some major Japanese companies, with large operations in the U.S., are even now talking about building, staffing, and operating their hospital and health-care facilities.

In summary, the American corporate world must find ways to bring to its employees a level of quality health care vastly improved from the level now operative—a quality that enables the totality of knowledge known at any point in time to be delivered promptly such that we have an enhanced chance of "doing it right the first time."

SEVENTEEN

The Purpose of the Church

Editor's note [from Presbyterian publication]: Mr. Donald M. Alstadt is President of Lord Corporation, Erie, Pennsylvania, and a Presbyterian layman. In recent years, he has conducted a number of seminars before church groups dealing with the human values in the management environment. He has occupied Church pulpits in dialogue with the clergy, and has met with faculty members of Princeton Theological Seminary to consider matters related to the purpose of the Church.

Individual members and clergy of our Christian church have, during recent years, been both perturbed and inspired by the increased involvement of their church in social action, "economic reform," urban rehabilitation, and many other causes directed toward improvement of the material welfare of individuals and in the sociological relationships of man and his brother.

Supporters of such involvement, priding themselves in going "where the action is," have often displayed much proactive attitude, at times even militant behavior, and at times courage—less capitulation to demand. They often condemn their brethren who contend that the

Speech originally given at Presbyterian Church of the Covenant, circa 1980, Erie, Penn., and later published in a Presbyterian publication.

church, as a body, should minimize its involvement in economic, social, and political affairs.

Individuals who resist the preoccupation of the church with civil problems, and prefer direction of the church programming and teaching toward the spiritual sphere of man's personal relationship to God, are frequently accused of merely displaying reactionary tendencies, desiring to maintain the status quo, displaying a selfish unconcern for their fellow man, and nostalgically longing for the good old "Rock of Ages" days long gone.

Recent doctrinal conflict within the concept structure of the church evidencing itself in "God is Dead" pronouncements, denials at last of the existence of such unnecessary ideas as divinity, sin, life after death, have, of course, helped convince the social and terrestrial reformers that they are putting the church into its relevant sphere of concern and action.

No one certainly would deny any person, clergy or layman, the right or responsibility, as an individual, to evidence concern or support for any effort designed to improve the relationships at the man-man interface, whether the issue be of a sociological, economic, or political origin. Nor would we even temper the right of an individual to be so involved if his motives be actuated not by an honest selfless concern for his brethren but by that gnawing guilt often displayed by a person whose economic or social position, are, in his own mind, not the result of his self-effort and sacrifice but the fortuitous circumstances of his birth or heritage. Such passions of guilt are, incidentally, unexcelled in their ability to deny the *right* of others to improve themselves with effort, dedication, and disappointment, in a manner that will maintain human dignity even if cast against the memory of sacrifice, pain, and frustration. We should always demand, however, that any help given a fellow man not prevent him from performing for himself those efforts which he inherently knows *he* must achieve, even with sacrifice, if he is to develop that level of self-imagery without which meaningful life cannot be long maintained.

There is, therefore, certainly no reason why a clergyman should not be involved in social reform; there is no reason also why an MD internist should not be involved in environmental pollution control, or the physicist in wildlife conservation. The clergyman, the internist, and the physicist must, however, recognize that their basic profession and training do not qualify them as experts in those fields in which they have suddenly become involved with new and perhaps even obsession-like concern.

Professional experts dealing with matters of urban analysis, for example, have indicated that many "intuitive measures proposed for urban improvement often intensify the very problems they are intended to alleviate and thus are detrimental in the long run." Jay Forrester of Massachusetts Institute of Technology, for one, contends that underemployment training programs and low-cost housing programs, although they seem promising and humane, may actually hasten degeneration of our communities.

Why have so many clergy, then, propelled themselves to, and forced their church's concern with, so many programs of social, economic, and urban reform and now find themselves involved with problems for which they possess the ardor—but not the expertise—for real contribution and assistance?

I suggest that the clergy have not run *to* anything; they have run away from that area of concern still characterized by unsurpassed importance to man, and unsurpassed as a responsibility of the clergy—the conceptual understanding of the interface between man and God. Clergy have many reasons, perhaps some unrecognized, for so doing. Probably no reason, however, is more real, if not admitted, than that many clergy no longer possess the intellectual awareness, the vigor of conceptual understanding, and the necessary courage of conviction to deal with the man-God relationship. Such involvement may, of course, be discouraged by the seeming conflicts resulting from the onslaught of the twentieth century science, technology, and knowledge explosion.

Long after the current crises in social and economic conflict have subsided, however, man will still be faced with those questions —"What am I? where am I going? what is my relevance in this cosmos?"—questions all asked not in relation to his fellow man but in relation to the infinite ordering forces within our universe. Even if man achieves only an increased awareness of "probabilities" as tentative answers to these questions, he will profit from an enhanced awareness of self—and self-discipline based on this self-awareness is indispensable to human freedom and progress.

The philosophical and "spiritual" implications of the "new physics" applicable to man's identity is, of course, not being ignored by the students of the physical sciences, and their enthusiastic concern with matters such as causality, free will, determinism, etc., is becoming increasingly apparent. Gustav Stromberg, the famous scientist and astronomer from Mt. Wilson Observatory, in his famous book *The Soul of the Universe* states, "the soul is indestructible and immortal; it carries an indelible record of its activities; it gives deity to the mental complex of man." Is physical science, as Arthur Compton suggested might happen years ago, usurping the dominions of a confused ecclesia? Continued efforts must be made, as Julian Huxley states, to "synthesize the physical and material world with the world of the mind and spirit, of the past with the future, of variety with unity, and the many with the one."

Such has been of concern to few clergymen, save de Chardin, but such concerns are vital issues if man is to develop an increased awareness of his relationship to his God and of his relationship to Chardin's "personal universe"—awarenesses that will allow an individual to project his existence beyond what may be the frustration of his immediate social or economic position. These awarenesses, not economic security or social tranquility, can produce a significant and rewarding human life. Such pursuit of awarenesses may continue to be of avocational concern to scientists; such matters would appear, however, to be the primary interest of the church. Indeed, such philosophical inquiry pursued with scientific knowledge as a handmaiden appear to be the unique responsibility of the church, and efforts related to such inquiry, syntheses, and subsequent teaching may be the only method by which the church may reestablish its real purpose and significance.

The church and its clergy alone can determine whether it has the intellectual discipline, the persistent courage, and the faith in its commitment that will allow the establishment of great and motivating philosophical principles in which, like those of the physical sciences, it can never be absolutely sure—but the high probability of which suggests inspiring implication.

EIGHTEEN

What Kind of Faith Will Serve Us Best?

WHAT KIND OF FAITH will serve us best? I suggest a faith
that is based on three postulates:

1. Reality of purpose in the universe.
2. Sovereignty of human personality.
3. Sanctity of method.
     A faith that believes that—
     a. There is a God dwelling in all nature and yet transcending
        it.
     b. God is near to man in all his needs, but beyond man's
        comprehension.
     c. Man is fashioned out of the Earth, but is nevertheless
        made in the spiritual image of God.
     d. Bound as he is in his physical limitation, he is unbounded
        in his spiritual and moral aspiration.
     e. The body and soul of Man are of God—and the whole of
        Man's body, mind, and soul are sacred.
     f. All men are equal in their essential humanity—and there
        is one moral law for all.
     g. Life is meaningful, and is a gracious gift of God.
     h. The ignorance in the world can be overcome—and in the
        overcoming of it one finds the real purpose of human life.
     i. Progress in the world is real if not uninterrupted.
     j. A Golden Age of human understanding awaits the human

race and can be hastened by the vision and effort of the human race.

k. Man's spiritual concern cannot be wholly concerned with life this side of the grave, because the anticipation of Hamlet's undiscovered border "puzzles the will" and is a vital and normal part of man's curiosity and intellectual desire.

With such a faith man can spread his adventuring sails and surge into his not always predictable destiny, confident that his high hopes will, from time to time find full meaning in the action of individual human courage and mutual human trust.

Love

Demands not
Envies not
Exploits not
Possesses not
Limits not
Reforms not
Covets not
Annoys not

Love

Cares
Inspires
Comforts
Dignifies
Unifies
Transforms self to beyond self
Relaxes
Is comfortable
Dwells in God